NNS Framework Year 5

Autumn and Summer

Oral and mental: e.g. counting, mental strategies, rapid recall 32–39, 48, 54–61

Unit	Days	Topic	Target Maths pages
1	3	Place value, ordering and rounding Using a calculator	2–11 68–69
2–3	10	Understanding × and + Mental calculation strategies (+ and ÷)	46, 47, 49, 50 54–61
		Pencil and paper procedures (× and ÷)	62–67
		Money and 'real life' problems Making decisions and checking results including using a calculataor	72–75 9, 38, 64, 65, 66, 69–73
4–5	10	Fractions, decimals and percentages	18–30
		Ratio and proportion	31
6	8	Handling data	114–119
		Using a calculator	68–69
7	2	Assess and review	120–126

Oral and mental: e.g. counting, mental strategies, rapid recall 32–39, 48, 54–61

Unit	Days	Topic	Target Maths pages
8–10	15	Shape and space Reasoning about shapes	92–113 92–113
		Measures, including problems	76–90
11	5	Mental calculation strategies (+ and −)	32–39
		Pencil and paper procedures (+ and −)	40–45
		Money and 'real life' problems Making decisions and checking results including using a calculator	72–75 9, 38, 64, 65, 66, 69–73
12	5	Properties of numbers	12–17
		Reasoning about numbers	71, 91, 127, 128
13	2	Assess and review	120–126
Total	60		

Spring

Oral and mental: e.g. counting, mental strategies, rapid recall 32–39, 48, 54–61

Unit	Days	Topic	Target Maths pages
1	3	Place value, ordering and rounding Using a calculator	2–11 68–69
2–3	10	Understanding × and ÷ Mental calculation strategies (× and ÷)	46, 47, 49, 50 54–61
		Pencil and paper procedures (× and ÷)	62–67
		Money and 'real life' problems Making decisions and checking results, including using a calculator	72–75 9, 38, 64, 65, 66, 69–73
4	5	Fractions, decimals and percentages	18–30
		Using a calculator	31
5	8	Shape and space	114–119
		Reasoning about shapes	68–69
6	2	Assess and review	120–126

Oral and mental: e.g. counting, mental strategies, rapid recall 32–39, 48, 54–61

Unit	Days	Topic	Target Maths pages
7–8	5	Measures, including problems	76–90
		Handling data	114, 119
9–10	10	Mental calculation strategies (+ and −)	32–39
		Pencil and paper procedures (+ and −)	40–45
		Money and 'real life' problems Making decisions and checking results including using a calculator	72–75 9, 38, 64, 65, 66, 69–73
11	5	Properties of numbers Reasoning about numbers	12–17 71, 91, 127, 128
12	2	Assess and review	120–126
Total	55		

The references are page numbers in Target Maths.

Numbers and the number system

Place value, ordering and rounding

2–4
- Read and write whole numbers in figures and words, and know what each digit represents.
(For decimals, see page 29.)

5
- **Multiply and divide any positive integer up to 10 000 by 10 or 100 and understand the effect.**
(e.g. 9900 ÷10, 737 ÷ 10, ÷10).

6–7
- Use the vocabulary of comparing and ordering numbers. including symbols such as <, >, , , =. Give one or more numbers lying between two given numbers. Order a set of integers less than 1 million.
(For decimals, see page 29.)

8–9
- Use the vocabulary of estimation and approximation. Make and justify estimates of large numbers, and estimate simple proportions such as one third, seven tenths. Round any integer up to 10 000 to the nearest 10, 100 or 1000. (For rounding decimals, see page 31.)

10–11
- **Order a given set of positive and negative integers** (e.g. on a number line, on a temperature scale.) Calculate a temperature rise or fall across 0 °C.

Properties of numbers and number sequences

12
- Recognise and extend number sequences formed by counting from any number in steps of constant size, extending beyond zero when counting back. For example: count on in steps of 25 to 1000, and then back; count on or back in steps of 0.1, 0.2, 0.3 …

13
- Make general statements about odd or even numbers, including the outcome of sums and differences.

14, 15
- Recognise multiples of 6, 7, 8, 9 up to the 10th multiple. Know and apply tests of divisibility by 2, 4, 5, 10 or 100.

17
- Know squares of numbers to at least 10×10.

16
- Find all the pairs of factors of any number up to 100.

Fractions and decimals

18–20
- Use fraction notation, including mixed numbers, and the vocabulary numerator and denominator.
Change an improper fraction to a mixed number (e.g. change $\frac{13}{10}$ to $1\frac{3}{10}$).
Recognise when two simple fractions are equivalent, including relating hundredths to tenths (e.g. $\frac{70}{100} = \frac{7}{10}$).

21
- Order a set of fractions such as 2, $2\frac{3}{4}$, $1\frac{3}{4}$, $2\frac{1}{2}$, $1\frac{1}{2}$ and position them on a number line.

27
- **Relate fractions to division**, and use division to find simple fractions, including tenths and hundredths, of numbers and quantities (e.g. $\frac{3}{4}$ of 12, $\frac{1}{10}$ of 50, $\frac{1}{100}$ of £3.

31
- Solve simple problems using ideas of ratio and proportion ('one for every…' and 'one in every…').

22–24
- **Use decimal notation for tenths and hundredths.**
Know what each digit represents in a number with up to two decimal places.
Order a set of numbers or measurements with the same number of decimal places.

25
- **Round a number with one or two decimal places to the nearest integer.**

26
- **Relate fractions to their decimal representations**: that is, recognise the equivalence between the decimal and fraction forms of one half, one quarter, three quarters… and tenths and hundredths (e.g. $\frac{7}{10} = 0.7$, $\frac{27}{100} = 0.27$).

28–30
- Begin to understand percentage as the number of parts in every 100, and find simple percentages of small whole-number quantities (e.g. 25% of £8).
Express one half, one quarter, three quarters, and tenths and hundredths, as percentages (e.g. know that $\frac{3}{4} = 75\%$).

Calculations

Rapid recall of addition and subtraction facts

34, 35
- Derive quickly or continue to derive quickly:
decimals that total 1 (e.g. 0.2 + 0.8) or 10 (e.g. 6.2 + 3.8);
all two digit pairs that total 100 (e.g. 43 + 57);
all pairs of multiples of 50 with a total of 1000 (e.g. 350 + 650).

Mental calculation strategies (+ and −)

36
- Find differences by counting up through next multiple of 10, 100 or 1000, e.g. **calculate mentally a difference such as 8006 − 2993.**

36
- Partition into H, T and U, adding the most significant digits first.

37
- Identify near doubles, such as 1.5 + 1.6.

37
- Add or subtract the nearest multiple of 10 or 100, then adjust.

32–33,
38
- Develop further the relationship between addition and subtraction.

38
- Add several numbers (e.g. four or five single digits, or multiples of 10 such as 40 + 50 + 80).

39
- Use known number facts and place value for mental addition and subtraction (e.g. 470 + 380, 810 − 380, 7.4 + 9.2, 9.2 − 8.6).

Pencil and paper procedures (+ and −)

40–45
- Use informal pencil and paper methods to support, record or explain additions and subtractions. **Extend written methods to: column addition/subtraction of two integers less than 10 000;** addition of more than two integers less than 10 000; addition or subtraction of a pair of decimal fractions, both with one or both with two decimale places (e.g. £29.78 = £53.34).

Understanding multiplication and division

46, 47
49, 50
- Understand the effect of and relationships between the four operations and the principles (not the names) of the arithmetic laws as they apply to multiplication. Begin to use brackets.

51,
52–53
- Begin to express a quotient as a fraction, or as a decimal when dividing a whole number by 2, 4, 5 or 10, or when dividing £p.
Round up or down after division, depending on the context.

Rapid recall of multiplication and division facts

48
- **Know by heart all multiplication facts up to 10×10.**

57, 59
- Derive quickly or continue to derive quickly:
division facts corresponding to 2, 3, 4, 5 and 10 times-tables;
division facts corresponding to tables up to 10×10;
doubles of all whole numbers 1 to 100 (e.g. 78×2);
doubles of multiples of 10 to 1000 (e.g. 670×10);
doubles of multiples of 100 to 10 000 (e.g. 6500×2);
and the corresponding halves.

Mental calculation strategies (× and ÷)

59
60–61
- Use doubling or halving, starting from known facts. For example: double/halve two-digit number by doubling/halving the tens first;
double one number and halve the other;
to multiply by 25, multiply by 100 then divide by 4;
find the ×16 table facts by doubling the ×8 table;
find sixths by halving thirds.

54
- Use factors (e.g. $8 \times 12 = 8 \times 4 \times 3$).

54, 55
- Use closely related facts (e.g. multiply by 19 or 21 by multiplying by 20 and adjusting; develop the ×12 table from the ×10 and ×2 tables).

55
- Partition (e.g. $47 \times 5 = (40 \times 6) + (7 \times 6)$).

46, 49
- Use the relationship between multiplication and division.

56–58
- Use known facts and place value to multiply and divide mentally.

Pencil and paper procedures (× and ÷)

62–67
- Approximate first. Use informal pencil and paper methods to support, record or explain multiplications and division.
Extend written methods to:
short multiplication of HTU or U.t by U:
long multiplication of TU by TU;
short division of HTU by U (with integer remainder).

Using a calculator

68–69
- Develop calculator skills and use a calculator effectively.

Checking results of calculations

69
- Check with the inverse operation when using a calculator.

38
- Check the sum of several numbers by adding in the reverse order.

65
- Check with an equivalent calculation.

9, 64,
66
- Estimate by approximating (round to nearest 10 or 100), then check result.

13
- Use knowledge of sums and differences of odd/even numbers.

Solving problems

Making decisions

70,
72–3
- Choose and use appropriate number operations to solve problems, and appropriate ways of calculating: mental, mental with jottings, written methods, calculator.
  (For examples of problems see pages 34–37, 82–89, 101.)

Reasoning and generalising about numbers or shapes

72–73,
120–125
- Explain methods and reasoning, orally and in writing.

91, 127,
128
- Solve mathematical problems or puzzles, recognise and explain patterns and relationships, generalise and predict. Suggest extensions by asking 'What if...?'

71
- Make and investigate a general statement about familiar numbers or shapes by finding examples that satisfy it. Explain a generalised relationship (formula) in words

Problems involving 'real life', money and measures

72–75
- **Use all four operations to solve simple word problems involving numbers and quantities** based on 'real life', money and measures **(including time)**, using one or more steps, including making simple conversions of pounds to foreign currency and finding simple percentages.
  Explain methods and reasoning.

Handling data

Organising and interpreting data

114,
115
- Discuss the chance of likelihood of particular events.

116–
119
- Solve a problem by representing and interpreting data in tables, charts, graphs and diagrams, including those generated by a computer, for example:
  bar line charts, vertical axis labelled in 2s, 5s, 10s, 20s or 100s, first where intermediate points have no meaning (e.g. scores on a dice rolled 50 times), then where they may have meaning (e.g. room temperature over time).

116–
117
- Find the mode of a set of data.

Measures, shape and space

Measures

76–83
- Use, read and write standard metric units (km, m, cm, mm, kg, g, l, ml), including their abbreviations, and relationships between them. Convert larger to smaller units (e.g. km to m, m to cm or mm, kg to g, l to ml).

76–83
- Suggest suitable units and measuring equipment to estimate or measure length, mass or capacity.
  Measure and draw lines to the nearest millimetre.
  Record estimates and readings from scales to a suitable degree of accuracy.

84–85
- **Understand area measured in square centimetres (cm^2). Understand and use the formula in words 'length × breadth' for the area of a rectangle.**
  Understand, measure and calculate perimeters of rectangles and regular polygons.

84–90
- Use units of time; read the time on a 24-hour digital clock and use 24-hour clock rotation, such as 19:53. Use timetables.

Shape and space

96–97
- **Recognise equilateral and isosceles triangles.**
  Classify triangles (isosceles, equilateral, scalene), using criteria such as equal sides, equal angles, lines of symmetry.

100–
102
- make shapes with increasing accuracy.
  Visualise 3-D shapes from 2-D drawings and identify different nets for an open cube.

103–
106
- Recognise reflective symmetry in regular polygons: for example, know that a square has four axes of symmetry and an equilateral triangle has three.
  Complete symmetrical patterns with two lines of symmetry at right angles (using squared paper or pegboard).
  Recognise where a shape will be after reflection in a mirror line parallel to one side (sides not all parallel or perpendicular to the mirror line).
  Recognise where a shape will be after a translation.

92–95
- Recognise positions and directions:
  read and plot co-ordinates in the first quadrant;
  recognise perpendicular and parallel lines.

107–
113
- Understand and use angle measure in degrees.
  Identify, estimate and order acute and obtuse angles.
  Use a protractor to measure and draw acute and obtuse angles to the nearest 5°.
  Calculate angles in a straight line.

pages 2 and 3

A

1 one thousand four hundred and thirty-one km
2 six thousand three hundred and fifty-six km
3 eight thousand one hundred and thirty-eight km
4 nine hundred and fifty-two km
5 eight thousand nine hundred and thirty-six km
6 three thousand five hundred and eight km
7 five thousand and seventeen km
8 ten thousand eight hundred and fifty-two km
9 nine hundred and twenty-eight km
10 seven thousand five hundred and seven km
11

City	Distance (km)
New York	5572
Moscow	2498
Paris	342
Los Angeles	8758
Johannesburg	971
Bombay	7190
Rio de Janeiro	9299
Buenos Aires	11131
Calcutta	7961
Toronto	5704

B

1

Seas	Area (sq. miles)
Pacific Ocean	64190000
Atlantic Ocean	33420000
Indian Ocean	28350000
Arctic Ocean	5110000
South China Sea	1148000
Caribbean Sea	1063000
Mediterranean Sea	966500
Baring Sea	875700
Gulf of Mexico	595800
Sea of Okhotsk	589800

2 one hundred and sixty-six million two hundred and forty thousand km^2
3 eighty-six million five hundred and sixty thousand km^2
4 seventy-three million four hundred and thirty thousand km^2
5 thirteen million two hundred and thirty thousand km^2
6 two million nine hundred and seventy-four thousand km^2
7 two million seven hundred and fifty-three thousand km^2
8 two million five hundred and three thousand km^2
9 two million two hundred and sixty-eight thousand one hundred and eighty km^2
10 one million five hundred and forty-two thousand nine hundred and eighty-five km^2
11 one million five hundred and twenty-seven thousand five hundred and seventy km^2

C

1 seven million seven thousand and ninety-one
2 nine hundred and fifty-three thousand one hundred and seventy-five
3 three million four hundred and seventy-two thousand and nine
4 two million two thousand one hundred and twenty-one
5 seventy-seven thousand four hundred
6 one million eight hundred and six thousand seven hundred and thirty-seven
7 nine million three hundred and nineteen thousand three hundred and sixty-seven
8 three hundred and two thousand seven hundred and forty-seven
9 twenty-seven thousand and sixty-three
10 two million six hundred and ninety-three thousand three hundred and eighty-three
11 three million seventy-two thousand nine hundred and twenty-two
12 five hundred and twenty-nine thousand and twenty-one
13 20579 twenty thousand five hundred and seventy-nine
20597 twenty thousand five hundred and ninety-seven
20759 twenty thousand seven hundred and fifty-nine
20795 twenty thousand seven hundred and ninety-five
20957 twenty thousand nine hundred and fifty-seven
20975 twenty thousand nine hundred and seventy-five
25079 twenty-five thousand and seventy-nine
25097 twenty-five thousand and ninety-seven
25709 twenty-five thousand seven hundred and nine
25790 twenty-five thousand seven hundred and ninety
25907 twenty-five thousand nine hundred and seven
25970 twenty-five thousand nine hundred and seventy

page 4

A

1 $300 + 60 + 9$
2 $1000 + 400 + 20 + 6$
3 $2000 + 100 + 90 + 3$
4 $4000 + 500 + 30 + 7$
5 $3000 + 800 + 50 + 8$
6 $600 + 70 + 2$
7 $5000 + 700 + 20 + 4$
8 $2000 + 900 + 10 + 7$
9 $1000 + 900 + 40 + 6$
10 $1000 + 100 + 50 + 6$
11 $8000 + 500 + 30 + 8$
12 $3000 + 500 + 30 + 2$

B

1 900
2 5
3 4000
4 70
5 80000
6 400
7 600000
8 8000
9 3000000

10 1
11 90 000
12 800 000
13 3000
14 200
15 5 000 000
16 17 672
17 104 813
18 149 628
19 273 497
20 30 813
21 1 575 628
22 424 157
23 1 173 684
24 12 716
25 332 176
26 1 818 534
27 6 159 019

C

1 377 496
2 1 863 031
3 2 003 193
4 42 584
5 1 150 267
6 1 194 805
7 1 007 436
8 5 215 320
9 1 029 754
10 2 187 362
11 804 189
12 608 174
13 600 005
14 21 298
15 135 165
16 1 204 471
17 88 362

page 5

A

1 300
2 1870
3 6200
4 7140
5 5930
6 580
7 3770
8 4000
9 9320
10 2080
11 4230
12 3800
13 660
14 7050
15 5410
16 4200
17 86
18 9
19 300
20 153
21 70
22 540
23 167
24 40
25 600
26 392
27 361
28 24
29 730
30 283
31 458
32 500

33 860×10
34 $620 \div 10$
35 139×10
36 $5800 \div 10$
37 201×10
38 $4170 \div 10$

B

1 9870
2 170
3 86 000
4 14
5 2600
6 203
7 80 000
8 230
9 9000
10 21 000
11 240 000
12 821
13 783×10
14 820×100
15 $3800 \div 10$
16 $130 000 \div 100$
17 1642×10
18 94×100
19 $620 000 \div 10$
20 $48 000 \div 100$
21 4300×10
22 $22 320 \div 10$
23 3500×100
24 $2 000 000 \div 100$

C

1 14 800
2 243 000
3 1 200 000
4 70 000
5 460 000
6 3 000 000
7 1 800 000
8 90 000
9 60
10 1970
11 10 000
12 23 600
13 80
14 600
15 4000
16 1709
17 275 400
18 27 540 000
19 2 754 000
20 2754
21 590 000
22 59
23 5 900 000
24 590
25 12 300
26 1230
27 1 230 000
28 123
29 200 000
30 2
31 200
32 2 000 000
33 140 000

pages 6 and 7

A

1 =
2 >
3 <
4 >
5 <
6 =
7 <
8 =
9 >
10 =
11 >
12 <
13 683, 863, 2386, 2836
14 1945, 5149, 5419, 5914
15 2743, 3247, 3274, 3472
16 1386, 1638, 1836, 1863
17 4578, 4758, 4785, 4857
18 6213, 6231, 6312, 6321
19 460
20 3275
21 2550
22 1655

B

1 <
2 =
3 <
4 =
5 <
6 >
7 <
8 =
9 >
10 =
11 <
12 >
13 3478, 3874, 4738, 4837
14 52 287, 52 783, 53 827, 53 872
15 19 162, 19 216, 19 261, 19612
16 10 606, 10 660, 16 006, 16 060
17 14 231, 14312, 14 321, 14421
18 30 003, 30 030, 30 033, 30 303
19 6750
20 54 270
21 23 625
22 4960
23 2900
24 12 000

C

1 >
2 =
3 =
4 <
5 >
6 <
7 <
8 =
9 <
10 =
11 <
12 >
13 a) 2 numbers which give a total of 16 173
    b) 2 numbers which give a total of 3825
    c) 8765 and 1234
    d) 5123 and 4876
14 3900
15 19 650
16 25 330
17 17 800
18 16 710
19 6980
20 33 150

page 8

A

1 4, 7
2 4, 12
3 5, 40
4 30, 50
5 100, 400
6 1, 4
7 a) Sammy
    b) Cyril
    c) Simon
8 Sammy 50 cm   Cecil 60 cm
    Cyril 80 cm   Simon 90 cm
    Sylvia 40 cm

B

1 140, 280
2 96, 108
3 $-5, -3$
4 10, 60
5 48, 60
6 a) Jacob
    b) James
    c) Jamie
7 James $\frac{3}{4}$ Jamie $\frac{9}{10}$
    Joe $\frac{1}{2}$ Jacob $\frac{1}{4}$

C

1 40, 140
2 $2\frac{1}{2}$, 4
3 $-7, -4$
4 $-60, -10$
5 $\frac{1}{5}, \frac{1}{2}$

page 9

A

1 60
2 30
3 30
4 50
5 80
6 100
7 70
8 20
9 40
10 70
11 60
12 40
13 800
14 200
15 500
16 300
17 300
18 700
19 500
20 700
21 300
22 900
23 400
24 1000

B

1 250
2 330
3 10
4 930
5 180
6 1000
7 500
8 1600
9 1100
10 2700
11 4000
12 300
13 700
14 11 000
15 16 000
16 13 000
17 8000
18 10 000
19 290
20 880
21 400
22 70
23 90
24 140
25 200
26 420
27 400
28 70

C

1 69 000	**5** 410	**9** 180
2 13 000	**6** 210	**10** 720
3 74 000	**7** 420	**11** 620
4 2 320 000	**8** 960	**12** 320

pages 10 and 11

A

1 1   **3** 3   **5** −3   **7** −6
2 −2   **4** 4   **6** −9   **8** −9
9 −5, −4, −3, −2, −1, 0, 1, 2
10 3, 2, 1, 0, −1, −2, −3
11 −12, −10, −8, −6, −4, −2, 0
12 −14, −10, −6, −2, 2, 6, 10
13 −7, −5, −3, −1, 1, 3, 5
14 5, 3, 1, −1, −3, −5, −7
15 −6, −4, −2, 0, 2, 4, 6
16 −6, −7, −8, −9, −10, −11, −12
17 A −2°C   **18** C   **19** a) 9°C   **20** a) −9°C
   B 7°C   b) 6°C   b) −3°C
   C −8°C   c) 15°C   c) 2°C

B

1 −11, −9, −7, −5, −3, −1, 1
2 −11, −8, −5, −2, 1, 4, 7
3 −6, −4, −2, 0, 2, 4, 6
4 −14, −10, −6, −2, 2, 6, 10
5 5, 3, 1, −1, −3, −5, −7
6 8, 6, 4, 2, 0, −2, −4
7 11, 8, 5, 2, −1, −4, −7
8 13, 9, 5, 1, −3, −7, −11
9 −6, −3, −1, 3, 7, 9
10 −8, −2, 0, 1, 4, 9
11 −7, −4, −1, 1, 2, 6
12 −6, −3, −2, 0, 3, 5
13 A −4°C   **14** B   **15** a) 10°C   **16** a) −18°C
   B −14°C   b) 20°C   b) 4°C
   C 16°C   c) 30°C   c) −1°C

C

1 A −48°C   B −32°C   C −8°C
   D 6°C   E 34°C
2 a) 14°C   b) 24°C   c) 42°C   d) 54°C
3 a) −14°C   b) −12°C   c) −34°C   d) 16°C

5

Old	Change	New
−4°C	+8°C	4°C
6°C	−11°C	−5°C
−23°C	+17°C	−6°C
12°C	−15°C	−3°C
−10°C	+9°C	−1°C
7°C	−20°C	−13°C

6

Old	Change	New
2°C	−5°C	−3°C
−5°C	+7°C	2°C
−11°C	+6°C	−5°C
10°C	−11°C	−1°C
−5°C	+15°C	10°C
−4°C	−10°C	−14°C

7

Old	Change	New
7°C	−10°C	−3°C
−5°C	−14°C	−19°C
−2°C	+16°C	14°C
3°C	−9°C	−6°C
0°C	−17°C	−17°C
8°C	−9°C	−1°C

page 12

A

1 23, 25, 27, 29, 31, 33
2 56, 48, 40, 32, 24, 16
3 125, 150, 175, 200, 225, 250
4 73, 68, 63, 58, 53, 48
5 47, 51, 55, 59, 63, 67
6 83, 76, 69, 62, 55, 48
7 59, 62, 65, 68, 71, 74
8 56, 48, 40, 32, 24, 16
9 5, 13, 21, 29, 37, 45
10 120, 117, 114, 111, 108, 105
11 21, 26, 31, 36, 41, 46
12 48, 42, 36, 30, 24, 18
13 19, 28, 37, 46, 55, 64
14 110, 90, 70, 50, 30, 10
15 21, 32, 43, 54, 65, 76

B

1 83, 85, 87, 89, 91, 93, 95
2 −1, −3, −5, −7, −9, −11, −13
3 25, 75, 125, 175, 225, 275, 325
4 28, 39, 50, 61, 72, 83, 94
5 68, 64, 60, 56, 52, 48, 44
6 325, 350, 375, 400, 425, 450, 475
7 0·2, 0·4, 0·6, 0·8, 1·0, 1·2, 1·4
8 −2, −6, −10, −14, −18, −22, −26
9 67, 62, 57, 52, 47, 42, 37
10 2·1, 1·8, 1·5, 1·2, 0·9, 0·6, 0·3
11 62, 55, 48, 41, 34, 27, 20
12 56, 49, 42, 35, 28, 21, 14
13 114, 215, 316, 417, 518, 619, 720
14 −45, −40, −35, −30, −25, −20, −15
15 68, 57, 46, 35, 24, 13, 2
16 0·5, 1·0, 1·5, 2·0, 2·5, 3·0, 3·5

C

1 101, 107, 113   **10** 0·09, 0·1, 0·11
2 −10, −12, −14   **11** 86, 94, 102
3 0·9, 1·1, 1·3   **12** 2, −2, −6
4 104, 113, 122   **13** 0·8, −0·2, −1·2
5 5, 0, −5   **14** 17, 10, 3
6 135, 160, 185   **15** 16, 4, −8
7 −5, −7, −9   **16** 81, 100, 119
8 1·25, 1·5, 1·75   **17** −5, −11, −17
9 88, 77, 66   **18** 132, 153, 174

page 13

A

1 123, 487, 631, 269, 885, 263
2 136, 318, 524, 312, 918, 574
3 125, 137, 489, 319, 525, 633, 271, 313, 887, 919, 265, 575
4 124, 138, 488, 320, 526, 632, 270, 314, 886, 920, 264, 576

B

1 even, even, even
2 even, even, even
3 odd, even, odd, even
4 odd, even, odd, even
5 even, even, even
6 even, even, even
7 odd, even, odd, even
8 odd, even, odd, even

C

1 odd **2** even **3** even **4** odd

page 14

A

1 4, 8, 12, 16, 20
2 5, 10, 15, 20, 25
3 10, 20, 30, 40, 50
4 6, 12, 18, 24, 30
5 9, 18, 27, 36, 45
6 20, 40, 60, 80, 100
7 Yes **13** Yes **19** No
8 No **14** No **20** Yes
9 Yes **15** Yes **21** No
10 No **16** No **22** Yes
11 No **17** Yes **23** Yes
12 Yes **18** Yes **24** No

B

1 106 **2** 54 **3** 46
4 69 **5** 46 **6** 64
7 14, 28, etc. **8** 12, 24, etc. **9** 15, 30, etc.
10 20, 40 etc. **11** 30, 60, etc. **12** 12, 24, etc.

C

1 24, 72, 3, 144, 45, 90, 27, 54, 96
2 24, 72, 144, 90, 54, 96
3 24, 72, 40, 144, 32, 96
4 72, 144, 45, 90, 27, 54
5 18, 36, 54, etc. **8** 28, 56, 84, etc.
6 24, 48, 72, etc. **9** 30, 60, 90, etc.
7 40, 80, 120, etc. **10** 24, 48, 72, etc.
11 16, 26, 36, 56, 86, 12, 32, 52, 62, 82, 18, 28, 38, 58, 68
12 12, 15, 18, 21, 36, 51, 63, 81
13 15, 25, 35, 65, 85 **18** 18, 36, 63, 81
14 16, 28, 32, 56 **19** 12, 28, 32, 36, 52, 56, 68
17 21, 28, 35, 56 **20** 12, 18, 36

page 15

A

1 True **6** False **11** False
2 False **7** True **12** True
3 True **8** False **13** False
4 False **9** True **14** False
5 True **10** False **15** True

B

1 600, 1000 **3** 18, 94, 1356 **5** 65, 830, 615
2 70, 900, 1320 **4** 68, 784, 236

C

Number	Divisible by				
	2	3	4	5	10
415	✗	✗	✗	✓	✗
648	✓	✓	✓	✗	✗
760	✓	✗	✓	✓	✓
834	✓	✓	✗	✗	✗
964	✓	✗	✓	✗	✗
1066	✓	✗	✗	✗	✗

page 16

A

1 1 and 6, 2 and 3 **4** 1 and 14, 2 and 7
2 1 and 8, 2 and 4 **5** 1 and 15, 3 and 5
3 1 and 12, 2 and 6, 3 and 4 **6** 1 and 18, 2 and 9, 3 and 6
7 1 and 20, 2 and 10, 4 and 5
8 1 and 25, 5 and 5
9 1 and 16, 2 and 8, 4 and 4
10 1 and 40, 2 and 20, 4 and 10, 5 and 8
11 1 and 36, 2 and 18, 3 and 12, 4 and 9, 6 and 6
12 1 and 100, 2 and 50, 5 and 20, 4 and 25, 10 and 10

B

1 1, 2, 4, 8, 16 **3** 1, 2, 3, 5, 6, 10, 15, 30
2 1, 3, 7, 21 **4** 1, 2, 3, 6, 9, 18, 27, 54
5 1, 2, 3, 4, 6, 8, 12, 16, 48
6 1, 7, 11, 77
7 1, 2, 4, 5, 8, 10, 16, 20, 40, 80
8 1, 2, 4, 8, 16, 32, 64
9 144 **11** 192 **13** 216 **15** 396
10 120 **12** 294 **14** 270 **16** 512

C

1 24 **4** 75 **7** 210 **10** 144 **13** 1150
2 60 **5** 36 **8** 72 **11** 324 **14** 1476
3 60 **6** 120 **9** 108 **12** 768 **15** 2592

page 17

A

1 4 9 16 25 36 49 64 81 100

B

1 4 9 16 25 36 49 64 81 100 121 144

C

1 25 **8** 61 **15** 14 **22** 47
2 36 **9** 32 **16** 16 **23** 27
3 49 **10** 36 **17** 18 **24** 50
4 64 **11** 28 **18** 40 **25** 87
5 121 **12** 130 **19** 25 **26** 134
6 169 **13** 20 **20** 30 **27** 243
7 25 **14** 15 **21** 38 **28** 418

page 18 and 19

A

1 $\frac{1}{4}, \frac{2}{8}$ **5** $\frac{1}{2}, \frac{5}{10}$ **9** $\frac{1}{3}, \frac{2}{6}$
2 $\frac{1}{5}, \frac{2}{10}$ **6** $\frac{3}{4}, \frac{6}{8}$ **10** $\frac{3}{5}, \frac{6}{10}$
3 $\frac{1}{3}, \frac{4}{12}$ **7** $\frac{1}{2}, \frac{3}{6}$ **11** $\frac{3}{4}, \frac{9}{12}$
4 $\frac{1}{2}, \frac{50}{100}$ **8** $\frac{3}{10}, \frac{30}{100}$ **12** $\frac{1}{4}, \frac{25}{100}$

B

1 $\frac{4}{8}$ **4** $\frac{4}{16}$ **7** $\frac{10}{16}$ **10** $\frac{6}{8}$ **13** $\frac{8}{16}$
2 $\frac{2}{6}$ **5** $\frac{2}{12}$ **8** $\frac{6}{12}$ **11** $\frac{8}{12}$ **14** $\frac{10}{12}$
3 $\frac{6}{10}$ **6** $\frac{2}{20}$ **9** $\frac{14}{20}$ **12** $\frac{16}{20}$ **15** $\frac{6}{20}$
16 $\frac{3}{4} = \frac{6}{8} = \frac{9}{12} = \frac{12}{16} = \frac{15}{20} = \frac{18}{24}$
17 $\frac{1}{6} = \frac{2}{12} = \frac{3}{18} = \frac{4}{24} = \frac{5}{30} = \frac{6}{36}$
18 $\frac{2}{5} = \frac{4}{10} = \frac{6}{15} = \frac{8}{20} = \frac{10}{25} = \frac{12}{30}$
19 $\frac{1}{8} = \frac{2}{16} = \frac{3}{24} = \frac{4}{32} = \frac{5}{40} = \frac{6}{48}$
20 $\frac{2}{3} = \frac{4}{6} = \frac{6}{9} = \frac{8}{12} = \frac{10}{15} = \frac{12}{18}$
21 $\frac{7}{10} = \frac{14}{20} = \frac{21}{30} = \frac{28}{40} = \frac{35}{50} = \frac{42}{60}$

C

1 $\frac{6}{9}$	5 $\frac{20}{25}$	9 $\frac{12}{30}$	13 $\frac{7}{10}$	17 $\frac{4}{9}$
2 $\frac{5}{20}$	6 $\frac{90}{100}$	10 $\frac{15}{60}$	14 $\frac{5}{6}$	18 $\frac{2}{3}$
3 $\frac{7}{14}$	7 $\frac{20}{100}$	11 $\frac{3}{4}$	15 $\frac{3}{5}$	19 $\frac{8}{20}$
4 $\frac{6}{18}$	8 $\frac{10}{15}$	12 $\frac{2}{5}$	16 $\frac{4}{7}$	20 $\frac{5}{8}$

page 20

A

1 $4\frac{1}{2}$, $\frac{9}{2}$ 5 $2\frac{3}{5}$, $\frac{13}{5}$ 9 $2\frac{3}{4}$, $\frac{11}{4}$

2 $2\frac{1}{3}$, $\frac{7}{3}$ 6 $4\frac{2}{3}$, $\frac{14}{3}$ 10 $4\frac{5}{6}$, $\frac{29}{6}$

3 $3\frac{1}{4}$, $\frac{13}{4}$ 7 $3\frac{1}{2}$, $\frac{7}{2}$ 11 $3\frac{1}{5}$, $\frac{16}{5}$

4 $1\frac{1}{6}$, $\frac{7}{6}$ 8 $1\frac{4}{5}$, $\frac{9}{5}$ 12 $2\frac{3}{8}$, $\frac{19}{8}$

B

1 $1\frac{2}{3}$	5 $3\frac{1}{8}$	9 $\frac{21}{4}$
2 $1\frac{3}{4}$	6 $4\frac{21}{100}$	10 $\frac{23}{5}$
3 $3\frac{1}{6}$	7 $\frac{7}{2}$	11 $\frac{37}{10}$
4 $2\frac{9}{10}$	8 $\frac{8}{3}$	12 $\frac{17}{6}$

C

1 $6\frac{1}{4}$	7 $6\frac{3}{9}$	13 $\frac{26}{5}$	19 $\frac{129}{10}$	
2 $5\frac{2}{3}$	8 $12\frac{3}{10}$	14 $\frac{16}{3}$	20 $\frac{47}{12}$	
3 $4\frac{5}{6}$	9 $5\frac{5}{12}$	15 $\frac{27}{4}$	21 $\frac{43}{9}$	
4 $5\frac{2}{7}$	10 $2\frac{16}{50}$	16 $\frac{57}{6}$	22 $\frac{708}{100}$	
5 $8\frac{4}{5}$	11 $7\frac{12}{100}$	17 $\frac{20}{7}$	23 $\frac{43}{16}$	
6 $6\frac{2}{8}$	12 $3\frac{17}{25}$	18 $\frac{57}{8}$	24 $\frac{477}{50}$	

page 21

A

1 $\frac{3}{6}$, $\frac{4}{8}$ 4 A $\frac{10}{100}$ D $\frac{7}{10}$ 5 a) $\frac{1}{2}$

2 $\frac{4}{10}$, $\frac{2}{6}$, $\frac{2}{5}$ B $\frac{2}{5}$ E $\frac{18}{20}$ b) $\frac{3}{4}$

3 $\frac{5}{8}$, $\frac{6}{10}$, $\frac{7}{12}$ C $\frac{1}{2}$ c) $\frac{1}{5}$

B

1 $\frac{3}{8}$, $\frac{1}{2}$, $\frac{3}{4}$ 3 $\frac{1}{2}$, $\frac{3}{5}$, $\frac{7}{10}$ 5 $\frac{2}{3}$, $\frac{9}{12}$, $\frac{5}{6}$

2 $\frac{1}{6}$, $\frac{1}{3}$, $\frac{1}{2}$ 4 $\frac{5}{8}$, $\frac{11}{16}$, $\frac{3}{4}$ 6 $\frac{2}{5}$, $\frac{9}{20}$, $\frac{5}{10}$

7 A $\frac{3}{20}$ C $\frac{30}{100}$ E $\frac{1}{2}$ G $\frac{7}{10}$

  B $\frac{1}{4}$ D $\frac{2}{5}$ F $\frac{30}{50}$ H $\frac{3}{4}$

C

1 $\frac{3}{4}$	3 $\frac{7}{10}$	5 $\frac{1}{4}$	7 $\frac{7}{16}$	9 $\frac{17}{40}$
2 $\frac{1}{2}$	4 $\frac{3}{8}$	6 $\frac{13}{20}$	8 $\frac{17}{24}$	10 $\frac{7}{24}$

11 number line from 0 to 1: $\frac{1}{12}$, $\frac{4}{12}$, $\frac{3}{8}$, $\frac{1}{2}$, $\frac{2}{3}$, $\frac{3}{4}$, $\frac{5}{6}$, $\frac{23}{24}$

pages 22 and 23

A

1 $\frac{9}{10}$, 0·9   3 $\frac{5}{10}$, 0·5   5 $\frac{6}{10}$, 0·6   7 $\frac{2}{10}$, 0·2

2 $\frac{1}{10}$, 0·1   4 $\frac{10}{10}$, 1·0   6 $\frac{3}{10}$, 0·3   8 $\frac{7}{10}$, 0·7

9 A 1·3 C 1·8 E 2·5

  B 1·6 D 2·2 F 2·9

10 0·4	13 2·9	16 10·5
11 1·7	14 6·8	17 17·2
12 3·3	15 0·6	18 4·1

B

1 $\frac{26}{100}$, 0·26   2 $\frac{93}{100}$, 0·93   3 $\frac{8}{100}$, 0·08   4 $\frac{65}{100}$, 0·65

5 A 0·12   C 0·18   E 0·25

  B 0·14   D 0·23   F 0·29

6 G 1·1   I 1·35   K 1·8

  H 1·2   J 1·65   L 1·95

7 $\frac{5}{10}$	11 $\frac{2}{100}$	15 $\frac{4}{10}$
8 8	12 $\frac{9}{10}$	16 $\frac{5}{100}$
9 40	13 $\frac{1}{10}$	17 $\frac{1}{100}$
10 6	14 $\frac{2}{100}$	18 $\frac{2}{10}$

19 0·06, 0·07, 0·08, 0·09, 0·1
20 1·1, 1·12, 1·14, 1·16, 1·18
21 1·97, 1·98, 1·99, 2·0, 2·01
22 1·01, 1·03, 1·05, 1·07, 1·09
23 0·85, 0·9, 0·95, 1·0, 1·05
24 4·02, 4·01, 4·0, 3·99, 3·98

C

1 1·652	11 0·072	21 $\frac{5}{1000}$
2 3·207	12 0·451	22 6
3 0·546	13 2·096	23 $\frac{1}{10}$
4 5·013	14 0·001	24 $\frac{3}{100}$
5 0·461	15 1·316	25 $\frac{8}{1000}$
6 4·204	16 6·09	26 9
7 0·03	17 1·048	27 $\frac{6}{100}$
8 0·263	18 4·005	28 $\frac{5}{1000}$
9 1·18	19 $\frac{6}{10}$	29 $\frac{1}{100}$
10 5·169	20 $\frac{7}{10}$	30 $\frac{9}{1000}$

page 24

A

1 7·0	4 21	7 7·0	10 5·4
2 35	5 1·1	8 3·0	11 57
3 4·0	6 25	9 8·0	12 5·0

13 number line from 0 to 2: 0·3 0·5 1·0 1·2 1·5 1·8

B

1 5·26, 5·62, 6·25, 6·5, 6·52
2 1·38, 1·8, 3·18, 3·8, 3·81
3 6·06, 6·07, 6·6, 6·7, 6·76
4 2·08, 2·18, 2·8, 21·8, 28
5 number line from 2·9 to 3·1: 2·91 2·95 2·98 3·0 3·04 3·06

C

1 0·45, 4·2, 4·25, 4·5, 4·52
2 0·67, 6·1, 6·17, 6·7, 6·71
3 0·39, 0·93, 3·09, 3·3, 3·39
4 8·22, 8·24, 8·4, 8·42, 8·44
5 1·17, 1·7, 1·71, 11·7, 17·1
6 3·33, 3·36, 3·63, 3·66, 33·3
7 2·2, 2·25, 2·52, 22·5, 25·2
8 4·464, 4·64, 4·644, 4·646, 4·66
9 number line from 2·9 to 3·0: 2·91 2·925 2·94 2·95 2·975 2·99

page 25

A

1 2	5 7	9 £12	13 £7
2 8	6 14	10 £6	14 £9
3 15	7 4	11 £6	15 £5
4 10	8 18	12 £4	16 £3

B

1 5	9 £9	17 6 m	25 4 kg
2 6	10 £27	18 4 m	26 4 kg
3 4	11 £4	19 10 m	27 12 kg
4 12	12 £6	20 6 m	28 9 kg
5 8	13 £13	21 3 m	29 5 kg
6 13	14 £8	22 1 m	30 3 kg
7 1	15 £4	23 8 m	31 16 kg
8 5	16 £10	24 12 m	32 8 kg

C

1.

Kilometres	Miles
1	0·6
2	1·2
3	1·9
4	2·5
5	3·1
6	3·7
7	4·4
8	5·0
9	5·6

2.

Litres	Gallons
1	0·2
2	0·4
3	0·7
4	0·9
5	1·1
6	1·3
7	1·5
8	1·8
9	2·0

page 26

A

1 True	4 False	7 True	10 False
2 False	5 False	8 False	11 True
3 True	6 False	9 True	12 False

13 $\frac{1}{2} = 0.5$ $\frac{5}{100} = 0.05$ $\frac{14}{100} = 0.14$

$\frac{4}{10} = 0.4$ $\frac{2}{10} = 0.2$ $\frac{1}{4} = 0.25$

B

1 $4\frac{68}{100}$	8 $8\frac{1}{10}$	15 8·75 km	22 0·78
2 $1\frac{17}{100}$	9 £1·46	16 17·09 km	23 0·4
3 $2\frac{1}{2}$	10 £2·25	17 0·9	24 0·58
4 $4\frac{3}{10}$	11 £5·04	18 0·03	25 0·77
5 $10\frac{3}{4}$	12 £3·18	19 0·3	
6 $6\frac{59}{100}$	13 1·4 m	20 0·63	
7 $8\frac{1}{100}$	14 3·61 m	21 0·7	

C

1 $1\frac{34}{100}$	9 $3\frac{7}{1000}$	17 £0·07
2 $6\frac{3}{4}$	10 $12\frac{51}{100}$	18 £1·15
3 $8\frac{4}{10}$	11 $16\frac{932}{1000}$	19 £4·60
4 $3\frac{197}{1000}$	12 $1\frac{46}{1000}$	20 £6·14
5 $2\frac{6}{100}$	13 1·09	21 2·09 m
6 $9\frac{281}{1000}$	14 8·25	22 0·076 km
7 $\frac{714}{1000}$	15 2·2	23 1·008 km
8 $5\frac{82}{1000}$	16 3·517	24 0·35 m

25 0·344, 0·43, $\frac{3}{4}$

26 $\frac{19}{100}$, $\frac{9}{10}$, 0·91

27 $\frac{27}{100}$, 0·5, $\frac{3}{5}$

28 0·188, 0·8, $\frac{81}{100}$

29 0·2, $\frac{27}{100}$, $\frac{2}{7}$

30 0·556, 0·56, $\frac{5}{6}$

31 $\frac{3}{10}$, 0·311, $\frac{1}{3}$

32 0·1, $\frac{101}{1000}$, $\frac{11}{100}$

page 27

A

1 3	9 2	17 3	25 2
2 8	10 6	18 5	26 8
3 2	11 5	19 7	27 6
4 5	12 9	20 4	28 9
5 7 cm	13 3 cm	21 6 cm	29 4 cm
6 10 cm	14 10 cm	22 9 cm	30 7 cm
7 4p	15 8p	23 10p	31 10p
8 10p	16 7p	24 8p	32 5p

B

1 40	7 20 cm	13 $\frac{1}{10}$	19 $\frac{1}{4}$
2 21	8 36 cm	14 $\frac{1}{20}$	20 $\frac{3}{4}$
3 27	9 70 cm	15 $\frac{7}{20}$	21 $\frac{1}{24}$
4 54	10 50p	16 $\frac{4}{5}$	22 $\frac{1}{6}$
5 35	11 25p	17 $\frac{1}{20}$	23 $\frac{1}{4}$
6 7	12 43p	18 $\frac{1}{5}$	24 $\frac{1}{3}$

C

1 280	9 140 g	17 $\frac{1}{50}$
2 48	10 600 ml	18 $\frac{1}{8}$
3 100	11 350 ml	19 $\frac{4}{5}$
4 1 m 80 cm	12 32 l	20 $\frac{1}{2}$
5 2 m 19 cm	13 $\frac{1}{50}$	21 $\frac{1}{365}$
6 8·1 cm	14 $\frac{9}{20}$	22 $\frac{1}{52}$
7 311 g	15 $\frac{99}{100}$	23 $\frac{5}{52}$
8 3·6 kg	16 $1\frac{1}{5}$	24 $\frac{30}{365}$

pages 28 and 29

A

	a)	b)	c)
1	$\frac{27}{100}$	0·27	27%
2	$\frac{8}{10}$	0·8	80%
3	$\frac{9}{100}$	0·09	9%
4	$\frac{1}{2}$	0·5	50%

5.

Fractions	Decimal	% age
$\frac{1}{2}$	0·5	50%
$\frac{1}{10}$	0·1	10%
1	1·0	100%
$\frac{1}{4}$	0·25	25%
$\frac{3}{4}$	0·75	75%
$\frac{1}{100}$	0·01	1%

6 10%	8 50%	10 20%
7 75%	9 1%	

B

	a)	b)	c)
1	$\frac{1}{2}$	0·5	50%
2	$\frac{7}{10}$	0·7	70%
3	$\frac{26}{100}$	0·26	26%
4	$\frac{1}{5}$	0·2	20%
5	$\frac{3}{4}$	0·75	75%
6	$\frac{72}{100}$	0·72	72%
7	$\frac{1}{4}$	0·25	25%
8	$\frac{2}{5}$	0·4	40%
9	$\frac{59}{100}$	0·59	59%

10 a) $\frac{1}{10}$　　b) 0·1　　c) 10%
11 a) $\frac{3}{10}$　　b) 0·3　　c) 30%
12 a) $\frac{8}{100}$　　b) 0·08　　c) 8%

C

1 a) 0·1　b) 10%　　**9** a) $\frac{1}{2}$　b) 0·5
2 a) 0·3　b) 30%　　**10** a) $\frac{91}{100}$　b) 0·91
3 a) 0·01　b) 1%　　**11** a) $\frac{9}{100}$　b) 0·09
4 a) 0·69　b) 69%　　**12** a) $\frac{9}{10}$　b) 0·9
5 a) 0·07　b) 7%　　**13** a) $\frac{4}{5}$　b) 0·8
6 a) 0·2　b) 20%　　**14** a) $\frac{19}{20}$　b) 0·95
7 a) 0·4　b) 40%　　**15** a) $\frac{3}{4}$　b) 0·75
8 a) 0·25　b) 25%　　**16** a) $\frac{39}{100}$　b) 0·39
17 17%　　　　**18** 59%
19

Subject	Total	Alison	Gary	Carly	Lee
English	100	61%	39%	58%	47%
Maths	200	70%	84%	35%	47%
Science	50	46%	72%	78%	84%
Geography	20	60%	55%	75%	70%
History	25	80%	76%	64%	52%

page 30

A

1 3	**7** 9	**13** 4	**19** 4	**25** £3·00
2 9	**8** 25	**14** 10	**20** 6	**26** 9p
3 6	**9** 21	**15** 6	**21** 20	**27** 20p
4 4	**10** 100	**16** 25	**22** 10	**28** £2·20
5 10	**11** 24	**17** 8	**23** 12	**29** 16p
6 7	**12** 35	**18** 50	**24** 30	**30** 40p

B

1 6	**6** 20	**11** 14p	**16** £1·32	**21** £27·00
2 18	**7** 30	**12** 30p	**17** £150	**22** 63p
3 12	**8** 32	**13** 66p	**18** 45p	
4 9	**9** £1·50	**14** £3·75	**19** £2·10	
5 36	**10** 3p	**15** 60p	**20** 36p	

C

1 40	**6** 74	**11** 200	**16** 200	**21** 9p
2 140	**7** 50	**12** 20	**17** £62·50	**22** 80p
3 80	**8** 50	**13** 80	**18** 10p	
4 20	**9** 250	**14** 25	**19** £14	
5 40	**10** 80	**15** 130	**20** 15p	

page 31

A

1

No. of weeks	No. of programmes	No. of weeks	No. of programmes
1	3	1	7
2	6	2	14
3	9	3	21
4	12	4	28
5	15	5	35
6	18	6	42
7	21	7	49
8	24	8	56
9	27	9	63
10	30	10	70

B

1 a) 4 white　　　**4** a) 3 white
　 b) 1 in every 5　　 b) 1 in every 4
2 a) 1 white　　　**5** a) 6 white
　 b) 1 in every 2　　 b) 1 in every 7
3 a) 7 white　　　**6** a) 2 white
　 b) 1 in every 8　　 b) 1 in every 3

C

1 450	**3** 36	**5** 35	**7** 9
2 12	**4** 48	**6** 25	**8** 120

page 32

A

1 63	**4** 294	**7** 121	**10** 4203
2 1400	**5** 73	**8** 98	**11** 92
3 82	**6** 54	**9** 953	**12** 83

B

1 53	**4** 270	**7** 75	**10** 3·5
2 73	**5** 795	**8** 645	**11** 0·2
3 0·6	**6** 3·5	**9** 750	**12** 53

C

1 0·32	**4** 3700	**7** 4800	**10** 0·2
2 2900	**5** 0·03	**8** 6·69	**11** 6·2
3 0·2	**6** 1·37	**9** 54·1	**12** 0·39

13 253, 3007, 3087, 3163, 4397, 4477, 4553, 7231, 7307, 7387

page 33

A

1 450	**4** 91	**7** 136	**10** 66
2 6	**5** 9	**8** 70	**11** 800
3 55	**6** 4993	**9** 6	**12** 43

B

1 9·0	**4** 240	**7** 302	**10** 570
2 0·4	**5** 582	**8** 3·7	**11** 725
3 835	**6** 0·37	**9** 5003	**12** 1·9

C

1 6·8	**9** 1·9	**17** 7500 − 3700
2 2·5	**10** 4·5	**18** 10·0 − 5·7
3 3·1	**11** 7·1	**19** 4·5 − 3·1
4 4·6	**12** 11·7	**20** 8000 − 5093
5 2·2	**13** 8200 − 2600	**21** 8·1 − 0·9
6 5·4	**14** 5000 − 3225	**22** 0·83 − 0·1
7 8·8	**15** 8·5 − 1·9	
8 4·5	**16** 7·0 − 2·72	

page 34

A

1 150	**4** 140	**7** 1600	**10** 1400
2 150	**5** 140	**8** 1600	**11** 1700
3 180	**6** 170	**9** 1500	**12** 1300

13 a) 82 + 18　18 + 82　　b) 750 + 250　250 + 750
　　　 53 + 47　65 + 35　　　 50 + 950　450 + 550
　　　 26 + 74　34 + 66　　　 950 + 50　550 + 450

B

1 1500	**4** 1400	**7** 1·8	**10** 1·6
2 1400	**5** 1500	**8** 1·3	**11** 1·7
3 1600	**6** 1400	**9** 1·6	**12** 1·5

13 a) $0.5 + 0.5$ $0.2 + 0.8$
  $0.1 + 0.9$ $0.8 + 0.2$
  $0.6 + 0.4$ $0.4 + 0.6$
b) $2.7 + 7.3$ $5.9 + 4.1$
  $8.3 + 1.7$ $6.4 + 3.6$
  $1.5 + 8.5$ $3.8 + 6.2$

C

1 $41 + 59$	**5** $260 + 740$	**9** $7200 + 2800$
2 $37 + 63$	**6** $650 + 350$	**10** $1300 + 8700$
3 $84 + 16$	**7** $590 + 410$	**11** $800 + 9200$
4 $16 + 84$	**8** $70 + 930$	**12** $5600 + 4400$

13 a) $0.27 + 0.73$ b) $7.9 + 2.1$
  $0.51 + 0.49$ $5.4 + 4.6$
  $0.46 + 0.54$ $2.1 + 7.9$
  $0.88 + 0.12$ $9.6 + 0.4$
  $0.15 + 0.85$ $0.2 + 9.8$
  $0.63 + 0.37$ $3.7 + 6.3$

page 35

A

1 $150 - 70$	**5** $140 - 60$	**9** $1500 - 600$
2 $160 - 90$	**6** $160 - 70$	**10** $1700 - 900$
3 $170 - 80$	**7** $1800 - 900$	**11** $1600 - 800$
4 $150 - 90$	**8** $1300 - 500$	**12** $1400 - 900$

13 a) $49 = 51$ b) $350 = 650$
  $51 = 49$ $550 = 450$
  $13 = 87$ $650 = 350$
  $26 = 74$ $850 = 150$
  $74 = 26$ $150 = 850$
  $67 = 33$ $250 = 750$

B

1 $1500 - 900$	**5** $1.6 - 0.9$	**9** $1.8 - 0.9$
2 $1700 - 800$	**6** $1.4 - 0.5$	**10** $1.6 - 0.8$
3 $1600 - 700$	**7** $1.7 - 0.9$	**11** $1.3 - 0.7$
4 $1500 - 800$	**8** $1.5 - 0.7$	**12** $1.5 - 0.6$

13 a) $0.2 = 0.8$ b) $5.6 = 4.4$
  $0.5 = 0.5$ $2.1 = 7.9$
  $0.3 = 0.7$ $4.7 = 5.3$
  $0.9 = 0.1$ $0.5 = 9.5$
  $0.1 = 0.9$ $7.2 = 2.8$
  $0.7 = 0.3$ $9.3 = 0.7$

C

1 $100 - 28$	**5** $1000 - 370$	**9** $10\,000 - 1700$
2 $100 - 65$	**6** $1000 - 520$	**10** $10\,000 - 9300$
3 $100 - 49$	**7** $1000 - 860$	**11** $10\,000 - 5200$
4 $100 - 71$	**8** $1000 - 40$	**12** $10\,000 - 8500$

13 a) $0.81 + 0.19$ b) $3.9 + 6.1$
  $0.25 + 0.75$ $5.3 + 4.7$
  $0.78 + 0.22$ $8.6 + 1.4$
  $0.34 + 0.66$ $0.2 + 9.8$
  $0.52 + 0.48$ $1.7 + 8.3$
  $0.16 + 0.84$ $6.4 + 3.6$

page 36 (counting up)

A

1 7	**3** 117	**5** 34	**7** 219	**9** 26
2 9	**4** 14	**6** 126	**8** 336	**10** 35

B

1 309	**3** 2013	**5** 218	**7** 5154	**9** 2025
2 423	**4** 3018	**6** 336	**8** 5018	**10** 3223

C

1 $728 - 437$	**6** $7000 - 3131$
2 $532 - 356$	**7** $6004 - 2039$
3 $641 - 258$	**8** $836 - 568$
4 $8000 - 5215$	**9** $8000 - 2323$
5 $5000 - 3216$	**10** $7005 - 3031$

page 36 (partitioning)

A

1 71	**3** 33	**5** 87	**7** 35	**9** 38
2 94	**4** 54	**6** 83	**8** 74	**10** 25

B

1 293	**3** 293	**5** 387	**7** 382	**9** 205
2 563	**4** 474	**6** 695	**8** 551	**10** 427

C

1 $376 - 319$	**6** $214 + 652$
2 $428 - 285$	**7** $157 - 90$
3 $257 + 189$	**8** $369 - 176$
4 $269 - 183$	**9** $365 + 168$
5 $546 - 394$	**10** $484 - 405$

page 37 (near doubles)

A

1 2.5	**3** 4.7	**5** 6.9	**7** 6.5	**9** 4.4
2 4.3	**4** 2.7	**6** 2.4	**8** 8.6	**10** 6.7

B

1 3.1	**3** 6.9	**5** 2.9	**7** 7.2	**9** 5.3
2 5.2	**4** 9.1	**6** 4.9	**8** 8.8	**10** 7.1

C

1 $2.8 + 2.8$	**6** $2.6 + 2.7$
2 $3.7 + 3.9$	**7** $4.6 + 4.7$
3 $4.8 + 4.6$	**8** $5.9 + 5.8$
4 $5.7 + 5.8$	**9** $7.7 + 7.5$
5 $3.8 + 3.6$	**10** $6.8 + 6.9$

page 37 (multiples of 10, 100, 1000)

A

1 92	**3** 154	**5** 112	**7** 159	**9** 139
2 56	**4** 122	**6** 66	**8** 68	**10** 89

B

1 549	**3** 383	**5** 555	**7** 2004	**9** 8012
2 396	**4** 281	**6** 576	**8** 1001	**10** 1007

C

1 $449 + 199$	**6** $2816 + 3012$
2 $663 - 299$	**7** $723 + 113$
3 $5293 + 2986$	**8** $771 - 198$
4 $872 + 111$	**9** $4349 + 2015$
5 $829 - 202$	**10** $467 + 298$

page 38 (+/− relationship)

A

1 $34 + 27 = 61$	**3** $19 + 48 = 67$
$27 + 34 = 61$	$48 + 19 = 67$
$61 - 27 = 34$	$67 - 19 = 48$
$61 - 34 = 27$	$67 - 48 = 19$
2 $84 - 58 = 26$	**4** $91 - 55 = 36$
$84 - 26 = 58$	$91 - 36 = 55$
$58 + 26 = 84$	$55 + 36 = 91$
$26 + 58 = 84$	$36 + 55 = 91$

B

1 124 + 217 = 341
217 + 124 = 341
341 − 217 = 124
341 − 124 = 217

5 340 + 160 = 500
160 + 340 = 500
500 − 160 = 340
500 − 340 = 160

2 106 − 43 = 63
106 − 63 = 43
63 + 43 = 106
43 + 63 = 106

6 800 − 370 = 430
800 − 430 = 370
430 + 370 = 800
370 + 430 = 800

3 168 + 39 = 207
39 + 168 = 207
207 − 39 = 168
207 − 168 = 39

7 14·6 + 7·9 = 22·5
7·9 + 14·6 = 22·5
22·5 − 14·6 = 7·9
22·5 − 7·9 = 14·6

4 293 − 52 = 241
293 − 241 = 52
241 + 52 = 293
52 + 241 = 293

8 3·9 − 1·4 = 2·5
3·9 − 2·5 = 1·4
2·5 + 1·4 = 3·9
1·4 + 2·5 = 3·9

C

1 136 + 118 = 254
118 + 136 = 254
254 − 118 = 136
254 − 136 = 118

5 417 + 229 = 646
229 + 417 = 646
646 − 229 = 417
646 − 417 = 229

2 206 − 149 = 57
206 − 57 = 149
149 + 57 = 149
57 + 149 = 206

6 303 − 235 = 68
303 − 68 = 235
235 + 68 = 303
68 + 235 = 303

3 380 + 640 = 1020
640 + 380 = 1020
1020 − 640 = 380
1020 − 380 = 640

7 260 + 470 = 730
470 + 260 = 730
730 − 260 = 470
730 − 470 = 260

4 1·8 + 4·6 = 6·4
4·6 + 1·8 = 6·4
6·4 − 4·6 = 1·8
6·4 − 1·8 = 4·6

8 2·3 + 1·2 = 3·5
1·2 + 2·3 = 3·5
3·5 − 1·2 = 2·3
3·5 − 2·3 = 1·2

page 38 (adding several numbers)

A

1 23	**3** 29	**5** 24	**7** 12	**9** 170
2 16	**4** 180	**6** 24	**8** 28	**10** 28

B

1 56	**3** 27	**5** 104	**7** 51	**9** 100
2 120	**4** 29	**6** 28	**8** 200	**10** 210

C

1 7	**3** 70	**5** 15	**7** 50	**9** 9
2 12	**4** 7	**6** 90	**8** 22	**10** 11

page 39

A

1

+	30	40	50
70	100	110	120
42	72	82	92
90	120	130	140

3

+	60	250	430
37	97	287	467
18	78	268	448
24	84	274	454

2

−	60	90	70
120	60	30	50
97	37	7	27
150	90	60	80

4

−	7	9	6
261	254	252	255
803	796	794	797
374	367	365	368

5

+	26	42	39
33	59	72	72
48	74	90	87
27	53	69	66

6

−	26	18	45
87	61	69	42
51	25	33	7
93	67	75	48

B

1 830	**10** 310	**19** 757	**28** 365
2 340	**11** 270	**20** 830	**29** +0·8
3 752	**12** 18	**21** 488	**30** +0·55
4 6·2	**13** 342	**22** 660	**31** +0·25
5 15	**14** 8·4	**23** 418	**32** +430
6 426	**15** 568	**24** 155	**33** +290
7 108	**16** 3·6	**25** 782	**34** +850
8 1256	**17** 386	**26** 222	
9 0·37	**18** 233	**27** 490	

C

1 3700 + 4600	**10** 6200 − 2400
2 9100 − 3200	**11** 0·7 − 0·33
3 0·3 + 0·45	**12** 8·23 + 0·07
4 0·8 − 0·41	**13** 9300 − 1700
5 4400 + 5300	**14** 3700 + 2500
6 8400 − 2600	**15** 4800 + 3400
7 4·76 + 0·24	**16** 8·62 + 0·38
8 4·51 + 0·09	**17** 0·83 − 0·55
9 0·16 + 0·5	**18** 4600 + 3700

19

+	0·6	0·16	1·66
0·3	0·9	0·46	1·96
0·13	0·73	0·29	1·79
0·05	0·65	0·21	1·71

20

−	0·3	0·9	0·05
2·0	1·7	1·1	1·95
4·6	4·3	3·7	4·55
8·45	8·15	7·55	8·4

page 40

A

1 384	**3** 303	**5** 529	**7** 482	**9** 275
2 529	**4** 766	**6** 652	**8** 812	

B

1 822	**6** 753
2 732	**7** 1503
3 1519	**8** 1634
4 2361	**9** 740
5 1077	**10** 3347 miles

C

1 4274	**6** 6363	**11** 7843
2 9846	**7** 8541	**12** 13 023
3 9939	**8** 7405	**13** £8322
4 6851	**9** 12 324	
5 4844	**10** 8345	

page 41

A

1 248	**4** 383	**7** 486	**10** 956
2 483	**5** 855	**8** 447	**11** 449
3 728	**6** 601	**9** 785	**12** 593

B

1 961	**4** 1646	**7** 2154	**10** 5377
2 1577	**5** 1149	**8** 2662	**11** £3131
3 1258	**6** 1139	**9** 3675	

c

1 4543	6 11 441	11 12 501	
2 5342	7 10 635	12 6932	
3 8561	8 13 864	13 £10 623	
4 13 446	9 11 851		
5 8482	10 12 347		

page 42

A

1 219	3 1993	5 £4·64
2 3871	4 £9·60	6 £8·32

B

1 2975	4 2668	7 £8·44	10 2·54 m
2 2249	5 £4·55	8 £8·69	11 6·1 m
3 4329	6 £6·20	9 3·5 m	12 1·49 m

c

1 7834	4 4947	7 15·86	10 0·89 m
2 6144	5 136·25	8 155·63	11 3·69 m
3 6444	6 20·72	9 2·0 m	12 22·02 m

page 43

A

1 268	4 625	7 256	10 832
2 512	5 637	8 816	11 292 miles
3 227	6 358	9 447	

B

1 282	4 460	7 235	10 113
2 140	5 303	8 139	11 591
3 437	6 49	9 583	12 327

c

1 204	5 3885	9 337	13 3214
2 724	6 1436	10 4309	14 £6799
3 2183	7 3286	11 2699	
4 2206	8 4756	12 3375	

page 44

A

1 108	5 208	9 525	13 628
2 377	6 438	10 769	
3 243	7 694	11 244	
4 566	8 886	12 539	

B

1 64	5 386	9 92	13 126
2 119	6 259	10 72	14 169
3 268	7 627	11 256	
4 277	8 277	12 458	

c

1 1516	5 458	9 1787	13 934
2 2158	6 757	10 3758	14 £2863
3 2695	7 2819	11 6163	
4 3764	8 1451	12 6799	

page 45

A

1 75	5 672	9 £1·19	13 £5·15
2 156	6 314	10 £2·56	
3 332	7 £2·64	11 £0·77	
4 328	8 £2·34	12 £3·57	

B

1 2806	5 1259	9 £4·67	13 37·9 kg
2 4158	6 6186	10 28·8	14 £4·66
3 1434	7 £1·86	11 14·6	
4 2355	8 £0·34	12 0·79	

C

1 32 691	5 41 043	9 3·74	13 21·73 secs.
2 20 947	6 75 402	10 16·48	
3 41 664	7 17·8	11 1·79	
4 52 655	8 11·43	12 7·42	

page 46

A

1

×6
5 → 30
8 → 48
4 → 24
9 → 54
7 → 42

3

×8
2 → 16
9 → 72
5 → 40
4 → 32
8 → 64

2

×7
3 → 21
6 → 42
9 → 63
5 → 35
8 → 56

4

×9
4 → 36
7 → 63
9 → 81
5 → 45
8 → 72

B

1 9×7	5 0.8×8	9 7×1.1	13 0.7×7
2 6×0	6 9×3	10 6×1	14 8×0.4
3 8×9	7 0.7×6	11 0.5×6	15 90×4
4 5×15	8 8×6	12 5×20	

16 $7 \times 9 = 63$
$9 \times 7 = 63$
$63 \div 9 = 7$
$63 \div 7 = 9$

17 $54 \div 9 = 6$
$54 \div 6 = 9$
$6 \times 9 = 54$
$9 \times 6 = 54$

18 $7 \times 8 = 56$
$8 \times 7 = 56$
$56 \div 8 = 7$
$56 \div 7 = 8$

19 $42 \div 7 = 6$
$42 \div 6 = 7$
$6 \times 7 = 42$
$7 \times 6 = 42$

20 $120 \div 6 = 20$
$120 \div 20 = 6$
$6 \times 20 = 120$
$20 \times 6 = 120$

21 $8 \times 14 = 112$
$14 \times 8 = 112$
$112 \div 14 = 8$
$112 \div 8 = 14$

22 $9 \times 15 = 135$
$15 \times 9 = 135$
$135 \div 15 = 9$
$135 \div 9 = 15$

23 $96 \div 8 = 12$
$96 \div 12 = 8$
$8 \times 12 = 96$
$12 \times 8 = 96$

24 $13 \times 8 = 104$
$8 \times 13 = 104$
$104 \div 8 = 13$
$104 \div 13 = 8$

25 $7 \times 0.5 = 3.5$
$0.5 \times 7 = 3.5$
$3.5 \div 7 = 0.5$
$3.5 \div 0.5 = 7$

C

1

×	9	7	10	6
8	72	56	80	48
3	27	21	30	18
9	81	63	90	54
7	63	49	70	42

2

×	5	9	6	8
8	40	72	48	64
7	35	63	42	56
4	20	36	24	32
9	45	81	54	72

3

×	4	6	9	7
6	24	36	54	42
8	32	48	72	56
5	20	30	45	35
7	28	42	63	49

4

×	3	6	8	7
9	27	54	72	63
4	12	24	32	28
5	15	30	40	35
8	24	48	64	56

page 47

A

1	40	3	36	5	35	7	42 m	9	80
2	18	4	120	6	88	8	100	10	160

B

1	56	3	450	5	208	7	72
2	147	4	7	6	30 m	8	63

C

1
a) 45
b) 196
c) 330
d) 1680
e) 175
f)

2 144
3 60 kg
4 91
5 £9600

page 48

A

1	6	13	20	25	7	37	6
2	16	14	28	26	5	38	8
3	18	15	36	27	6	39	4
4	0	16	24	28	8	40	7
5	14	17	4	29	3	41	10
6	12	18	32	30	9	42	9
7	30	19	30	31	9	43	9
8	18	20	40	32	4	44	6
9	21	21	25	33	7	45	4
10	27	22	15	34	10	46	8
11	12	23	50	35	5	47	10
12	24	24	35	36	8	48	7

49

×	9	3	7
6	54	18	42
8	72	24	56
4	36	12	28

B

1

×6
4 → 24
8 → 48
6 → 36
1 → 6
5 → 30
0 → 0
7 → 42
9 → 54

3

×8
8 → 64
0 → 0
5 → 40
4 → 32
1 → 8
6 → 48
9 → 72
7 → 56

2

×7
6 → 42
0 → 0
7 → 49
9 → 63
8 → 56
4 → 28
1 → 7
5 → 35

4

×9
5 → 45
7 → 63
9 → 81
10 → 91
4 → 36
8 → 72
0 → 0
6 → 54

C

1	5.4	10	4.8	19	0.6	28	6.4 ÷ 8
2	4.8	11	0.5	20	0.6	29	8 × 7
3	3.5	12	0.8	21	0.9 × 4	30	5 × 0.7
4	54	13	0.7	22	8 × 5	31	4.9 × 7
5	4.0	14	9	23	7.2 ÷ 9	32	42 ÷ 6
6	42	15	0.9	24	6.3 ÷ 7	33	0.9 × 8
7	6.4	16	7	25	0.5 × 9	34	0.7 × 4
8	5.6	17	0.7	26	20 × 20	35	2.4 ÷ 3
9	28	18	0.5	27	48 ÷ 6	36	8.1 ÷ 9

page 49

A

÷6
30 → 5
54 → 9
36 → 6
24 → 4
48 → 8
42 → 7

÷7
21 → 3
56 → 8
35 → 5
63 → 9
28 → 4
49 → 7

÷8
16 → 2
64 → 8
56 → 7
24 → 3
72 → 9
48 → 6

÷9
90 → 10
36 → 4
81 → 9
18 → 2
54 → 6
72 → 8

B

1	81 ÷ 9	6	54 ÷ 9	11	100 ÷ 20	16	500 ÷ 50
2	77 ÷ 11	7	120 ÷ 20	12	24 ÷ 10	17	30 ÷ 15
3	5 ÷ 10	8	14 ÷ 1	13	80 ÷ 4	18	15 ÷ 10
4	48 ÷ 8	9	200 ÷ 8	14	85 ÷ 10	19	120 ÷ 15
5	42 ÷ 6	10	45 ÷ 5	15	8 ÷ 1	20	72 ÷ 12

C

21 72 ÷ 12 = 6
72 ÷ 6 = 12
6 × 12 = 72
12 × 6 = 72

22 5 × 15 = 75
15 × 5 = 75
75 ÷ 15 = 5
75 ÷ 5 = 15

23 96 ÷ 16 = 6
96 ÷ 6 = 16
6 × 16 = 96
16 × 6 = 96

24 $21 \times 8 = 168$ **25** $7 \times 19 = 133$
$8 \times 21 = 168$ $19 \times 7 = 133$
$168 \div 8 = 21$ $133 \div 7 = 19$
$168 \div 21 = 8$ $133 \div 19 = 7$

c

1

Input		Output
7·2	÷9	0·8
300	÷15	20
210	÷7	30
0·8	÷1	0·8
4	÷8	0·5
60	÷100	0·6
92	÷10	9·2
11	÷1	11

2

Input		Output
3	÷100	0·03
4·8	÷6	0·8
25	÷10	2·5
5·6	÷7	0·8
10	÷4	2·5
7·2	÷8	0·9
4	÷100	0·04
320	÷8	40

3

Input		Output
75	÷1	75
500	÷20	25
6	÷12	0·5
81	÷9	9
8·1	÷9	0·9
13	÷100	0·13
6·3	÷7	0·9
10	÷40	0·25

4 45

page 50

A

1 9	**4** 3	**7** 6	**10** 18
2 6	**5** 5	**8** 12 each	**11** 20
3 7	**6** 25	**9** 9	**12** £15

B

1 12	**3** 12	**5** 25
2 8	**4** 400 g	**6** £12·50

c

1 15	**4** 80p	**7** 25
2 18 cm	**5** £12·50	
3 84	**6** 55	

page 51

A

1 $16\frac{1}{2}$	**7** $6\frac{3}{5}$	**13** £7·25	**19** £1·20
2 $14\frac{3}{5}$	**8** $9\frac{1}{4}$	**14** £5·60	**20** £7·80
3 $6\frac{1}{3}$	**9** $7\frac{2}{3}$	**15** £5·75	**21** 15·5 cm
4 $13\frac{7}{10}$	**10** $12\frac{2}{5}$	**16** £13·50	**22** £3·40
5 $6\frac{3}{4}$	**11** £8·50	**17** £4·75	**23** £11·50
6 $10\frac{1}{2}$	**12** £7·70	**18** £11·40	

B

1 $20\frac{3}{4}$	**9** $6\frac{41}{100}$	**17** £2·30
2 $5\frac{4}{7}$	**10** $3\frac{5}{7}$	**18** £2·40
3 $8\frac{1}{9}$	**11** 23·5	**19** £4·55
4 $6\frac{2}{6}$	**12** 31·75	**20** £1·35
5 $5\frac{11}{25}$	**13** 26·2	**21** £68·40
6 $21\frac{4}{5}$	**14** 42·7	**22** 28·75 litres
7 $5\frac{3}{8}$	**15** 23·25	
8 $17\frac{3}{10}$	**16** £1·60	

c

1 $86 \div 7$	**9** $131 \div 8$	**17** 17·3
2 $39 \div 8$	**10** $120 \div 7$	**18** 12·3
3 $73 \div 9$	**11** $335 \div 4$	**19** 15·8
4 $95 \div 6$	**12** $101 \div 12$	**20** 14·5
5 $1491 \div 100$	**13** 23·5	**21** 16·7
6 $157 \div 6$	**14** 13·7	**22** 17·4
7 $167 \div 10$	**15** 18·8	
8 $172 \div 9$	**16** 12·9	

pages 52 and 53

A

1 7	**3** 6	**5** 7	**7** 13	**9** 6
2 7	**4** 14	**6** 7	**8** 15	**10** 8

B

1 7	**3** 17	**5** 33	**7** 13	**9** 8
2 12	**4** 14	**6** 23	**8** 9	**10** 7

C

1 16	**3** 12	**5** 6	**7** 13	**9** 29
2 34	**4** 33	**6** 14	**8** 17	**10** 26

page 54 (using factors)

A

1 42	**3** 132	**5** 56	**7** 14	**9** 8
2 72	**4** 54	**6** 7	**8** 6	**10** 3

B

1 90	**3** 156	**5** 15	**7** 126	**9** 8
2 96	**4** 16	**6** 21	**8** 153	**10** 15

C

1 208	**3** 357	**5** 243	**7** 18	**9** 15
2 450	**4** 312	**6** 9	**8** 17	**10** 17

page 54 (working out times-tables)

B

12 24 36 48 60 72 84 96 108 120

C

17 34 51 68 85 102 119 136 153 170

page 55 (multiplying by 19/21)

A

1 126	**3** 117	**5** 154	**7** 153	**9** 198
2 144	**4** 121	**6** 198	**8** 171	**10** 176

B

1 152	**5** 231	**9** 494	**13** 247	**17** 294
2 228	**6** 336	**10** 378	**14** 456	**18** 567
3 285	**7** 323	**11** 483	**15** 361	**19** 399
4 147	**8** 418	**12** 441	**16** 532	**20** 504

c

1	637 ÷ 49	6	765 ÷ 51
2	612 ÷ 51	7	1485
3	1089 ÷ 99	8	1616
4	1414 ÷ 101	9	882
5	784 ÷ 49	10	969

page 55 (partitioning)

A

1	39	3	72	5	76	7	87	9	112
2	54	4	48	6	92	8	96	10	132

B

1	136	3	252	5	224	7	188	9	336
2	285	4	168	6	288	8	190	10	245

c

A

1	372 ÷ 6	6	774 ÷ 9
2	602 ÷ 7	7	45 ÷ 6
3	511 ÷ 7	8	40·6 ÷ 7
4	472 ÷ 8	9	40·2 ÷ 6
5	672 ÷ 8	10	73·6 ÷ 8

page 56

A

1	350	9	200	17	2700	25	60
2	520	10	40	18	6400	26	2
3	810	11	700	19	700	27	10
4	1740	12	80	20	4600	28	9
5	2690	13	300	21	5100	29	40
6	3860	14	500	22	800	30	80
7	670	15	60	23	9000	31	3
8	2900	16	900	24	3800	32	70

B

1	12 000	9	300	17	60 × 800
2	21 000	10	58	18	2700 ÷ 100
3	12 000	11	4	19	90 × 600
4	35 000	12	620	20	9000 ÷ 1000
5	24 000	13	90	21	40 × 600
6	36 000	14	5	22	4300 ÷ 10
7	30 000	15	760	23	60 × 700
8	28 000	16	3	24	8900 ÷ 100

c

1

÷10
4350 → 435
1260 → 126
840 → 84
6000 → 600

4

×60
700 → 42 000
400 → 24 000
8000 → 480 000
900 → 54 000

2

÷100
9800 → 98
2700 → 27
600 → 6
7000 → 70

5

×90
400 → 36 000
800 → 72 000
6000 → 540 000
1500 → 135 000

3

÷1000
7000 → 7
42 000 → 42
510 000 → 510
30 000 → 30

page 57

A

1	30	8	130	15	150	22	60	29	100
2	40	9	60	16	260	23	90	30	140
3	80	10	110	17	40	24	45	31	80
4	50	11	70	18	55	25	50	32	125
5	90	12	160	19	75	26	70	33	540 m
6	120	13	220	20	35	27	65	34	250
7	190	14	180	21	85	28	95		

B

1	540	10	360	19	475 × 2
2	670	11	425	20	710 ÷ 2
3	350	12	255	21	390 × 2
4	510	13	75 × 2	22	670 ÷ 2
5	720	14	290 ÷ 2	23	185 × 2
6	970	15	265 × 2	24	330 ÷ 2
7	135	16	580 ÷ 2	25	£280
8	165	17	295 × 2		
9	245	18	550 ÷ 2		

c

1

Double
95 → 190
445 → 990
640 → 1280
785 → 1570
970 → 1940
415 → 830
690 → 1380
875 → 1750
945 → 1890

2

Halve
750 → 375
870 → 435
1560 → 780
1630 → 815
1790 → 895
470 → 235
980 → 490
1720 → 860
1550 → 775

3 a) 2048   b) 256

page 58

A

1	160	7	210	13	36	19	95
2	270	8	320	14	42	20	68
3	400	9	270	15	75	21	54
4	450	10	700	16	52	22	75
5	120	11	300	17	57	23	120
6	800	12	240	18	72	24	92

B

1	350	7	270	13	34 × 5	19	900 × 4
2	4200	8	192	14	28 × 4	20	90 × 6
3	240	9	70 × 6	15	52 × 9	21	36 × 3
4	2400	10	800 × 9	16	43 × 6	22	13 × 6
5	432	11	60 × 8	17	800 × 5	23	33 × 5
6	224	12	600 × 6	18	70 × 2	24	22 × 4

c

1

×6
700 → 420
6000 → 36 000
87 → 522
8000 → 48 000
600 → 3600
63 → 378
79 → 474
9000 → 54 000
54 → 324

2

×7
8000 → 56 000
79 → 553
66 → 462
7000 → 49 000
600 → 4200
55 → 385
900 → 6300
98 → 686
5000 → 35 000

3

×8
6000 → 48 000
94 → 752
79 → 632
700 → 5600
9000 → 72 000
36 → 288
800 → 6400
67 → 536
4000 → 32 000

4

×9
9000 → 81 000
49 → 441
57 → 513
6000 → 54 000
700 → 6300
85 → 765
500 → 4500
78 → 702
8000 → 72 000

5 £400 6 368 7 63 000 miles

page 59

A

1 70	9 560	17 49	25 84	33 92
2 46	10 6200	18 29	26 114	34 56
3 94	11 5400	19 440	27 172	35 88
4 84	12 9800	20 470	28 96	36 79
5 36	13 17	21 380	29 128	37 97
6 72	14 23	22 1800	30 146	38 82
7 880	15 37	23 4800	31 196	39 69
8 780	16 26	24 3900	32 158	40 86

B

1 104	7 1740	13 280	19 172
2 134	8 18 600	14 790	20 270
3 118	9 46	15 6400	21 109
4 130	10 42	16 9800	22 177
5 1680	11 58	17 324	23 118
6 15 200	12 81	18 274	24 171

C

1 730×2	9 5800×2	17 9.8×2
2 970×2	10 9900×2	18 0.9×2
3 690×2	11 6.2×2	19 0.56×2
4 76×2	12 8.4×2	20 0.75×2
5 $1100 \div 2$	13 $13\,800 \div 2$	21 $17.8 \div 2$
6 $1320 \div 2$	14 $15\,600 \div 2$	22 $1.24 \div 2$
7 $1940 \div 2$	15 $14.8 \div 2$	23 $0.96 \div 2$
8 $16\,600 \div 2$	16 $7.4 \div 2$	24 $1.52 \div 2$

pages 60 and 61

A

1 12 24 36 48 60 72 84 96 108 120

2 68	6 190	10 480
3 104	7 320	11 540
4 132	8 280	12 168
5 210	9 340	13 440

14 15	15 14	16 32	17 20
30	28	16	10
60	56	8	5
120	112		
240	224		

B

1 14 28 42 56 70 84 98 112 126 140

2 90	9 272	16 480
3 120	10 182	17 315
4 230	11 738	18 252
5 2050	12 312	19 399
6 1800	13 490	20 294
7 4150	14 400	21 483
8 3350	15 540	22 546

23 300	26 33	29 25
150	16·5	12·5
24 9	27 70	30 38
4·5	35	19
25 180	28 4·2	
90	2·1	

C

1 770	7 546	13 112
2 780	8 564	14 208
3 840	9 900	15 304
4 1710	10 450	16 352
5 368	11 650	17 496
6 486	12 1350	18 448

19 60	22 3	25 43	28 0·06
30	1·5	21·5	0·03
15	0·75		
20 22	23 5	26 9	29 2·7
11	2·5	4·5	1·35
5·5	1·25		
21 1000	24 25	27 3·5	30 0·1
500	12·5	1·75	0·05
250	6·25		

page 62

A

1 117	5 112	9 200	13 152
2 116	6 140	10 378	14 270
3 102	7 138	11 301	15 261
4 144	8 105	12 232	16 245

B

1 1458	5 3940	9 2184	13 1805
2 2625	6 2188	10 3717	14 2628
3 1512	7 1204	11 1998	
4 3432	8 1696	12 2856	

C

1 119 925	4 112 301	7 65 148	10 254 624
2 85 808	5 117 876	8 87 078	
3 183 690	6 130 924	9 138 375	

page 63

A

1 296	4 716	7 992
2 768	5 3807	8 1390
3 1404	6 3724	9 3168

B

1 880	5 1912	9 501	13 3648
2 1806	6 1544	10 1542	14 2436
3 1494	7 4606	11 1215	15 4145
4 3114	8 1647	12 2303	16 2312

C

1 1458	4 19 544	7 27 552	10 21 092
2 3438	5 21 932	8 23 832	11 26 094
3 14 776	6 25 875	9 30 072	12 17 667

page 64

A

1 338	3 336	5 378	7 377
2 348	4 420	6 630	8 690

B

1 2312	**3** 2484	**5** 4056	**7** 624	**9** 2006
2 1314	**4** 2990	**6** 1776	**8** 2175	**10** 1700

C

1 2432	**5** 4693	**9** 10 817	**13** 13·104 kg
2 11 362	**6** 8640	**10** 23 712	
3 6156	**7** 8352	**11** £11 376	
4 13 870	**8** 10 878	**12** £10 244	

page 65

A

1 8·6	**3** 27·6	**5** 29·1
2 15·6	**4** 24·0	**6** 22·8

B

1 23·7	**5** 24·3	**9** 30·6	**13** 6·4 km
2 25·8	**6** 34·4	**10** 17·4	**14** 52·2 litres
3 19·6	**7** 26·8	**11** 48·0	**15** 57·6 kg
4 57·4	**8** 39·0	**12** 24·5	

C

1 7·74	**5** 1·96	**9** 51·6	**13** 25·28 m
2 11·8	**6** 38·01	**10** 27·54	**14** 61·25 l
3 13·56	**7** 44·04	**11** 38·52	**15** 13·65 l
4 46·26	**8** 3·84	**12** 13·9	**16** 8·9 km

page 66

A

1 18	**7** 17 r 2	**13** 13 r 4	
2 17	**8** 15 r 1	**14** 17 r 2	
3 12 r 2	**9** 13 r 3	**15** 22 r 2	
4 17 r 4	**10** 22 r 2	**16** 16 r 1	
5 23 r 1	**11** 16 r 2	**17** 84	
6 14 r 2	**12** 18 r 3		

B

1 21 r 2	**7** 27 r 5	**13** 41 r 6	
2 15 r 3	**8** 29 r 2	**14** 31 r 6	
3 22 r 5	**9** 37 r 5	**15** 38 r 8	
4 21 r 5	**10** 32 r 6	**16** 66 r 3	
5 14 r 3	**11** 43 r 1	**17** 23	
6 28 r 2	**12** 35 r 1	**18** 26	

C

1 25 r 5	**6** 25 r 13	**11** 16 r 16
2 22 r 8	**7** 21 r 7	**12** 26 r 7
3 21 r 6	**8** 36 r 15	**13** 23 g
4 32 r 10	**9** 27 r 3	**14** £34
5 19	**10** 36	**15** 29

page 67

A

1 24	**6** 19	**11** 49	**16** 17
2 16	**7** 32	**12** 14	**17** 14
3 17	**8** 14	**13** 44	**18** £16
4 17	**9** 34	**14** 22	**19** 76
5 26	**10** 14	**15** 19	**20** £67

B

1 23	**6** 26 r 1	**11** 47 r 1	**16** 92 r 5
2 44 r 6	**7** 28	**12** 38 r 6	**17** 210
3 31 r 2	**8** 76 r 3	**13** 48 r 2	**18** 67 g
4 47	**9** 33 r 3	**14** 38 r 6	
5 57 r 5	**10** 52 r 5	**15** 66 r 2	

C

1 27	**7** 15
2 27	**8** 37
3 23	**9** 29
4 34	**10** 16
5 43	**11** 19 packs 6 left over
6 35	**12** 26

page 68

A

1 −5	**6** −21	**11** £7·65	**16** £6·40
2 −8	**7** −29	**12** £5·58	**17** 222
3 −15	**8** −22	**13** £6·30	**18** 423
4 −16	**9** £3·44	**14** £10·70	**19** 235
5 −13	**10** £4·57	**15** £7·50	**20** 148

B

1 −15	**6** −37	**11** £4·87	**16** £2·60
2 −17	**7** −76	**12** £7·77	**17** 30·0
3 −56	**8** −35	**13** £33·60	**18** 100·0
4 −43	**9** £3·84	**14** £34·80	**19** 19·0
5 −51	**10** £5·75	**15** £3·60	**20** 39·0

C

1 −5·5	**6** −4·59	**11** 50·0	**16** £26·80
2 −4·15	**7** −6·23	**12** 28·0	**17** £32·10
3 −2·71	**8** −6·66	**13** £3·80	**18** £3·80
4 −3·46	**9** 21·68	**14** £3·92	**19** £2·54
5 −2·56	**10** 27·0	**15** £13·80	**20** £2·36

page 69

A

1 86 + 89	**8** 375 − 127	c) 105, 106
2 184 + 59	**9** 318 − 169	d) 137, 138
3 165 + 53	**10** 146 + 137	**14** −22°C
4 56 + 67	**11** 712 − 248	**15** £33·60
5 135 − 78	**12** 633 − 254	**16** 2454
6 247 − 86	**13** a) 32, 33	
7 253 − 78	b) 71, 72	

B

1 1·37 + 1·23	**6** 5·28 − 1·67	c) 64, 65, 66
2 2·58 + 1·61	**7** 2·42 − 1·63	d) 73, 74, 75
3 3·49 + 0·86	**8** 4·22 − 2·37	**10** 1542
4 1·64 + 1·64	**9** a) 26, 27, 28	**11** 36
5 3·45 − 1·75	b) 37, 38, 39	**12** −53°C

C

1 209	**2** £2830·50	**3** 54 m	**4** £1·35
5 30 611	**6** a) 16 b) 19 c) 23 d) 37		

page 70 (top half)

A

1 ×	**3** +	**5** −	**7** ×
2 −	**4** ÷	**6** +	**8** ÷

B

1 ×	**3** −	**5** ×	**7** ÷
2 +	**4** −	**6** ÷	**8** +

C

1 ÷	**3** +	**5** ×	**7** +
2 −	**4** ×	**6** −	**8** ÷

16

pages 72 and 73

A
1 9 | 3 56 | 5 140 | 7 18 | 9 720
2 72 | 4 55 | 6 120 | 8 16 | 10 84

B
1 175 or 176
2 12
3 142
4 5
5 231
6 125
7 80
8 4
9 1440
10 32

C
1 50
2 1500
3 61 737
4 156
5 2307
6 268
7 7
8 18 000
9 229
10 25

pages 74 and 75

A
1 £43·20, £6·80
2 £28·30, £21·70
3 £36·15, £13·85
4 £37·50, £12·50
5 £38·10, £11·90
6 75p
7 22p
8 25p
9 £15·00
10 £1·10
11 £9·00
12 8
13 6
14 table tennis bat
15 football shirt
16 170
17 117

B
1 £49·40, £50·60
2 £99·00, £1·00
3 £93·20, £6·80
4 £87·90, £12·10
5 £25·20, £74·80
6 £2·25
7 £1·54
8 £1·25
9 £22·00
10 £198·00
11 £75·00
12

U.K. (pound)	S. Africa (rand)	U.S.A. (dollar)	Japan (yen)
£1·00	10	1·6	170
£10·00	100	16	1700
£50·00	500	80	8500
£300·00	3000	480	51 000

C
1 £491·40, £8·60
2 £468·00, £32·00
3 £475·20, £24·80
4 £101·00, £399·00
5 £255·60, £244·40
6 26
7 13
8 leather football
9

U.K. (pound)	India (rupee)	Europe (Euro)	Israel (shekel)
£1·00	69	1·64	6·15
£10·00	690	16·4	61·5
£80·00	5520	131·2	492
£200·00	13 800	328	1230

pages 76 and 77

A
1 500 m
2 600 m
3 1·1 km
4 3·7 km
5 150 cm
6 80 cm
22 0·25 km
23 33 mm
7 2·5 m
8 1·4 m
9 3 mm
10 27 mm
11 1·5 cm
12 3·1 cm
24 0·8 m
25 14·6 cm
13 cm
14 mm
15 m
16 mm
17 km
18 cm
26 6 km
27 0·5 m

B
1 2700 m
2 1380 m
3 3·6 km
4 2·57 km
5 140 cm
6 361 cm
23 <
24 =
7 5·28 m
8 2·17 m
9 29 mm
10 15 mm
11 0·3 cm
12 9·8 cm
25 >
26 =
13 mm
14 km
15 m
16 mm
17 cm
18 km
27 <
28 >

C

1
mm	m
1	0·001
2480	2·48
7	0·007
150	0·150

3
m	km
287	0·287
3281	3·281
1594	1·594
2300	2·3

2
cm	m
6	0·06
159	1·59
130	1·3
47	0·47

4
mm	cm
30	3
4	0·4
17	1·7
1	0·1

5 140 mm
6 42 000 m
7 0·3 m
8 80 000 m
9 0·4 km
10 0·12 m
11 0·4 m, 404 mm, 44 cm, 0·004 km
12 380 cm, 38 m, 0·338 km, 0·38 km
13 5·5 mm, 0·05 m, 55 mm, 0·5 m
14 0·007 km, 0·02 km, 2007 cm, 27 m
15 109 cm, 9000 mm, 109 m, 0·19 km

page 78

A
1 1·43 m
2 1·15 m
3 5 m
4 25
5 4·8 km
6 9·7 cm

B
1 250 m
2 2·12 m
3 166 m
4 19·2 cm
5 30 m
6 1·66 m

C
1 92 cm
2 1·82 m
3 30
4 3·6 km
5 1147 km
6 8·4 cm

page 79

A
1 20 kg, 35 kg: 15 kg
2 10 g, 50 g: 40 g
3 50 mm, 90 mm: 40 mm
4 5 m, 25 m: 20 m
5 15 l, 30 l: 15 l
6 25 ml, 100 ml: 75 ml
7 640 g, 740 g: 100 g
8 34 cm, 42 cm: 8 cm
9 5 l, 10 l: 5 l
10 500 ml, 750 ml: 250 ml

B

1 40 g, 60 g: 20 g		**6** 300 ml, 450 ml: 150 ml	
2 8 kg, 10·5 kg: 2·5 kg		**7** 1·6 kg, 2·7 kg: 1·1 kg	
3 3·2 cm, 3·9 cm: 0·7 cm		**8** 67 g, 82 g: 15 g	
4 55 mm, 80 mm: 25 mm		**9** 0·25 l, 0·5 l: 0·25 l	
5 0·5 l, 3 l: 2·5 l		**10** 125 ml, 375 ml: 250 ml	

C

1 400 g. 900 g: 500 g   **6** 0·55 l, 0·73 l: 0·18 l
2 0·75 kg, 1·5 kg: 0·75 kg   **7** 0·38 kg, 0·46 kg: 0·08 kg
3 32 cm, 46 cm: 14 cm   **8** 0·28 m, 0·54 m: 0·26 m
4 0·03 m, 0·06 m: 0·03 m   **9** 1·3 l, 2·7 l: 1·4 l
5 4·35 l, 5·25 l: 0·9 l   **10** 125 ml, 600 ml: 475 ml

page 80

A

1	2000 g	**5**	0·75 kg	**9**	3750 g	**13**	g
2	1500 g	**6**	5·2 kg	**10**	800 g	**14**	kg
3	250 g	**7**	1·25 kg	**11**	0·4 kg	**15**	g
4	1900 g	**8**	2·4 kg	**12**	5·5 kg	**16**	kg

B

1	3000 g	**5**	2·48 kg	**9**	6250 g	**13**	kg
2	1750 g	**6**	0·8 kg	**10**	1800 g	**14**	g
3	600 g	**7**	3·5 kg	**11**	4·35 kg	**15**	kg
4	2960 g	**8**	0·62 kg	**12**	0·94 kg	**16**	g

C

1

g	kg
1386 → 1·386
600 → 0·6
5160 → 5·16
4000 → 4
2980 → 2·98
641 → 0·641

2

kg	g
6·5 → 6500
0·075 → 75
3·25 → 3250
0·394 → 394
3·7 → 3700
0·045 → 45

3 3·5 kg   **5** 70 kg
4 10 g   **6** 0·4 kg

page 81

A

1 1·6 kg   **3** 82·8 kg   **5** 25 g
2 500 g   **4** 3·75 kg   **6** 1·4 kg

1·25 kg

B

1 300 kg   **3** 270 g   **5** 350 g
2 1·8 kg   **4** 2 kg   **6** 1·9 kg

C

1 32 g   **3** 120 kg   **5** 1·32 kg
2 1·14 kg   **4** 375 g   **6** 250 g

page 82

A

1 1000 ml   **10** 600 ml
2 1250 ml   **11** 0·4 l
3 750 ml   **12** 3·75 ml
4 2300 ml   **13** litres
5 3 l   **14** ml
6 2·5 l   **15** ml
7 0·25 l   **16** litres
8 1·9 l   **17** ml
9 3500 ml   **18** litres

B

1	5000 ml	**6**	0·7 l	**11**	2·25 l	**16**	ml
2	2750 ml	**7**	1·89 l	**12**	0·48 ml	**17**	litres
3	4320 ml	**8**	5·9 l	**13**	litres	**18**	litres or ml
4	370 ml	**9**	6500 ml	**14**	ml		
5	2·38 l	**10**	1800 ml	**15**	ml		

C

1

ml	litres
2280 → 2·28
1347 → 1·347
510 → 0·51
4000 → 4
2940 → 2·94
1681 → 1·681

2

ml	litres
0·9 → 900
3·92 → 3920
2·156 → 2156
4·659 → 4659
0·042 → 42
0·78 → 780

3 0·15 l   **5** 0·3 l   **7** 250 ml
4 10 000 ml   **6** 40 l   **8** 100 l

page 83

A

1 750 ml   **3** 400 ml   **5** 6 litres
2 300 ml   **4** 1·7 l   **6** 160 ml

B

1 1·15 l   **3** 8·4 l   **5** 25 days
2 1·8 l   **4** 3·5 l   **6** 80

C

1 200 ml   **3** 3·6 l   **5** 40   **7** 1·475 ml
2 400 ml   **4** 11·7 l   **6** 21 l

pages 84 and 85

A

1 10 cm   **4** a) 28 cm   **5** 36 cm^2 **9** 20 cm
2 12 cm   b) 24 cm   **6** 35 cm^2 **10** 24 cm^2
3 10 cm   c) 18 cm   **7** 16 cm^2
             d) 20 cm   **8** 36 cm^2

B

1 34 cm   **2** 42 cm   **3** 18 cm   **4** 72 cm
5

Length	5 cm	7 cm	8 cm	7 cm	8 cm	9 cm
Breadth	4 cm	3 cm	5 cm	7 cm	3 cm	4 cm
Perimeter	18 cm	20 cm	26 cm	28 cm	22 cm	26 cm
Area	20 cm^2	21 cm^2	40 cm^2	49 cm^2	24 cm^2	36 cm^2

8 2500 m^2

C

1 a) 22 cm   **3** a) 54 cm
   b) 21 cm^2 b) 126 cm^2
2 a) 36 cm   **4** a) 24 cm
   b) 44 cm^2 b) 23 cm^2
5

Length	12 cm	13 cm	9 cm	3·5 cm	6 cm	8 cm
Breadth	11 cm	8 cm	6 cm	4 cm	2·5 cm	6 cm
Perimeter	46 cm	42 cm	30 cm	15 cm	17 cm	28 cm
Area	132 cm^2	104 cm^2	54 cm^2	14 cm^2	15 cm^2	48 cm^2

6 10 000   **8** 1 000 000
7 100   **9** £480

pages 86 and 87

A

1	420	**5**	21	**9**	40
2	255	**6**	56	**10**	300
3	5	**7**	$\frac{1}{2}$	**11**	2
4	$2\frac{1}{2}$	**8**	$\frac{2}{3}$	**12**	$\frac{1}{2}$

13 a) 31   c) 31   e) 62
    b) 30   d) 30   f) 61
14 28 days in February. Not a leap year.
15 a) Thursday   c) Saturday
    b) Tuesday   d) Sunday
16 Monday
17 2nd November
18 6th July

B

1	480	**5**	156	**9**	4
2	345	**6**	104	**10**	$\frac{1}{2}$
3	7	**7**	9	**11**	230
4	$3\frac{1}{2}$	**8**	2600	**12**	250

13 a) 6th May   **14** a) Sunday
    b) 2nd October   b) Wednesday
    c) 8th January   c) Friday
    d) 2nd November   d) Tuesday

15

APRIL						
Su	M	Tu	W	Th	F	Sa
					1	2
3	4	5	6	7	8	9
10	11	12	13	14	15	16
17	18	19	20	21	22	23
24	25	26	27	28	29	30

C

1 True   **4** False
2 True   **5** False
3 False
6 a) 14th November   **7** a) Friday
    b) 13th July   b) Saturday
    c) 2nd January   c) Sunday
    d) 30th April   d) Monday

8

Su	M	Tu	W	Th	F	Sa
	1	2	3	4	5	6
7	8	9	10	11	12	13
14	15	16	17	18	19	20
21	22	23	24	25	26	27
28	29	30	31			

9 a) 52   b) 1
10 a) Wednesday   b) Saturday

pages 88 and 89

A

1 a) 10 past 3   b) 3:10 p.m.
2 a) 6 mins. to 10   b) 9:54 a.m.
3 a) 25 past 2   b) 2:25 a.m.
4 a) 23 mins. to 7   b) 6:37 p.m.
5 a) 3 mins. past 12   b) 12:03 p.m.
6 a) 11 mins. to 5   b) 4:49 a.m.
7 a) 12 mins. past 7   b) 7:12 p.m.
8 a) 2 mins. to 6   b) 5:58 a.m.
9 a) 21 mins. past 1   b) 1:20 p.m.
10 a) quarter to 12   b) 11:45 p.m.

11 a) 17 mins. past 2   b) 2:17 a.m.
12 a) 22 mins. to 9   b) 8:38 a.m.
13 1 a) 3:19 p.m.   b) 3:04 p.m.
    2 a) 10:03 a.m.   b) 9:48 a.m.
    3 a) 2:34 a.m.   b) 2:19 a.m.
    4 a) 6:46 p.m.   b) 6:31 p.m.
    5 a) 12:12 p.m.   b) 11:57 a.m.
    6 a) 4:58 a.m.   b) 4:43 a.m.
    7 a) 7:21 p.m.   b) 7:06 p.m.
    8 a) 6:07 a.m.   b) 5:52 a.m.
    9 a) 1:29 p.m.   b) 1:14 p.m.
   10 a) 11:54 p.m.   b) 11:39 p.m.
   11 a) 2:26 a.m.   b) 2:11 a.m.
   12 a) 8:47 a.m.   b) 8:32 a.m.

B

1

TIME IN WORDS	12-HOUR CLOCK	24-HOUR CLOCK
three o'clock	3:00 p.m.	15:00
quarter to 8	7:45 a.m.	07:45
half past 8	8:30 p.m.	20:30
25 to 11	10:35 a.m.	10:35
8 minutes to 4	3:52 a.m.	03:52
19 minutes past 10	10:19 p.m.	22:19
23 minutes to 10	9:37 a.m.	09:37
16 minutes past 6	6:16 p.m.	18:16
28 minutes past 11	11:28 a.m.	11:28
7 minutes to 6	5:53 p.m.	17:53

2 0, 15, 30, 25, 8   41, 23, 44, 32, 7
3 a) 14:25   21:44   b) 15:14   10:33
      07:10   9:02   07:59   9:51
      19:55   17:41   20:44   18:30
      10:00   10:53   10:49   11:42
      03:17   17:18   04:06   18:57

C

1 a) 13 mins. to 9   b) 8:47 a.m.   c) 08:47
2 a) 23 mins. past 2   b) 2:23 p.m.   c) 14:23
3 a) 1 min. to 1   b) 12:59 a.m.   c) 00:59
4 a) 28 mins. to 12   b) 11:32 p.m.   c) 23:32
5 a) 18 mins. past 11   b) 11:18 a.m.   c) 11:18
6 a) 4 mins. past 5   b) 5:04 p.m.   c) 17:04
7 a) 23 mins. to 1   b) 12:37 p.m.   c) 12:37
8 a) 27 mins. to 9   b) 8:33 p.m.   c) 20:33
9 15h 13 mins.   12h 42mins.
    9h 37 mins.   6h 56mins.
    23h 1 min.   11h 23mins.
    0h 28 mins.   3h 27mins.

10

	Sunrise	Sunset	Daylight length
Jan 2nd	08:06	16:03	7h 57 mins
March 6th	06:36	17:49	11h 13 mins
May 1st	05:34	20:23	14h 49 mins
July 3rd	04:49	21:20	16h 31 mins
Sept 4th	06:17	19:41	13h 24 mins
Nov 6th	07:02	16:26	9h 24 mins

page 90

A

1 a) 25 mins.	b) 45 mins.	c) 1h 6 mins.		
2 7			**4** 11:35	**6** 12:52
3 09:54			**5** 15 mins.	

B

1 a) 1h 42 mins.	b) 2h 32 mins.	c) 3h 43 mins.		
2 2			**4** 09:21	**6** 12:01
3 14:07			**5** 27 mins.	

C

1 a) 41 mins.	b) 1h 29 mins.	c) 2h 32 mins.		
2 2			**4** 13:17	**6** 15:31
3 16:34			**5** 53 mins.	

page 91

A

¹3	²6		³6	⁴7
⁵1	2	⁶8		7
7		⁷4	⁸5	
	⁹2		¹⁰2	¹¹1
¹²5	7		¹³5	0

B

¹3	²9	8		³5	⁴4
⁵5	8		⁶7	6	2
	⁷3	⁸6	2		6
⁹2		4		¹⁰1	
¹¹4	¹²3		¹³2	0	¹⁴5
¹⁵8	9	2		¹⁶7	5

C

¹4	²7	³2		⁴9	⁵1
⁶9	8	4		⁷6	0
	⁸6	0	⁹8		0
¹⁰3			¹¹7	¹²4	9
¹³9	¹⁴2	4		4	
¹⁵5	0		¹⁶1	2	1

pages 92 and 93

A

1 What do you call a man with a spade   Doug

2 A isoceles triangle   C right-angled triangle
B Square   D rectangle

B

1 RGQS

2 Why does y go up? Because x is a cross

C

1 What do you call a one eyed dinosaur?
Doyouthinktheysaurus.

2 A isosceles triangle   C right-angled triangle
B rectangle   D square

pages 94 and 95

A

1 A1   G3   M1   N1   O4   Q4
T0   V1   W3   XO   YO   Z1

2 NOYZ

B

2 a) 9
b) 6 of equal length, 3 longer diagonals are also
equal
c) at the centre

C

2

Shape	Diagonals
quadrilateral	2
pentagon	5
hexagon	9
heptagon	14
octagon	20

3 a) 27   b) 35   c) 44   d) 54

pages 96 and 97

A

1 (See table in B for names of shapes.)

2 1, 8, 10, 12, 15, 16

B

No.	Shape	Sides	Equal sides	Equal angles
1	irregular pentagon	5	0	0
2	equilateral triangle	3	3	3
3	regular octagon	8	8	8
4	irregular quadrilateral	4	0	0
5	scalene triangle	3	0	0
6	square	4	4	4
7	regular pentagon	5	5	5
8	irregular hexagon	6	4 and 2	2 pairs
9	isosceles triangle	3	2	2
10	irregular heptagon	7	2	2
11	rectangle	4	2 pairs	4
12	irregular pentagon	5	0	0
13	regular hexagon	6	6	6
14	right-angled triangle	3	0	0
15	irregular quadrilateral	4	0	0
16	irregular octagon	8	4 pairs	4 pairs

20

c

1 No. 3 – 4 pairs   No. 11 – 2 pairs
No. 6 – 2 pairs   No. 13 – 3 pairs
No. 8 – 2 pairs   No. 16 – 3 lines
No. 10 – 2 pairs

pages 98 and 99

A

1 (See table in B for names of shapes.)
2 a) cylinder, sphere, cone, hemi-sphere
b) tetrahedron, cube, octahedron
c) pentagonal prism, triangular prism, cuboid, cube, hexagonal prism
d) triangular prism, square-based pyramid

B

No.	Shape	Flat Faces	Edges	Vertices
1	tetrahedron	4	6	4
2	pentagonal prism	7	15	10
3	cylinder	2	2	0
4	sphere	0	0	0
5	triangular prism	5	9	6
6	cone	1	1	1
7	square based pyramid	5	8	5
8	cuboid	6	12	8
9	hemi-sphere	1	1	0
10	cube	6	12	8
11	hexagonal prism	8	18	12
12	octahedron	8	12	6

c

1 4 triangles
2 5 rectangles, 2 pentagons
3 2 circles
4 no flat faces
5 2 triangles, 3 rectangles
6 1 circle
7 4 triangles, 1 square
8 6 rectangles
9 1 circle
10 6 squares
11 6 rectangles, 2 hexagons
12 8 triangles

page 102

A

1 6   **5** 15   **9** 11   **13** 8
2 8   **6** 9   **10** 11   **14** 11
3 6   **7** 9   **11** 13   **15** 7
4 7   **8** 13   **12** 14

B

1 6   **5** 15   **9** 19   **13** 10
2 8   **6** 9   **10** 5   **14** 39
3 10   **7** 3   **11** 23   **15** 17
4 5   **8** 3   **12** 10

c

1 4   **5** 5   **9** 7   **13** 7
2 3   **6** 5   **10** 5   **14** 7
3 3   **7** 3   **11** 10   **15** 8
4 5   **8** 5   **12** 5

page 103

B

Shape	Sides	Lines of symmetry
equilateral triangle	3	3
square	4	4
regular pentagon	5	5
regular hexagon	6	6
regular octagon	8	8

pages 108 to 112

A

1 70°   **17** 80°   **33** acute
2 60°   **18** 130°   **34** obtuse
3 80°   **19** 70°   **35** acute
4 125°   **20** 120°   **36** obtuse
5 130°   **21** 30°   **37** acute
6 140°   **22** 80°   **38** obtuse
7 30°   **23** 110°   **39** acute 20°
8 95°   **24** 150°   **40** acute 70°
9 60°   **25** 50°   **41** obtuse 130°
10 30°   **26** 160°   **42** acute 40°
11 100°   **27** 10°   **43** obtuse 110°
12 170°   **28** 120°   **44** obtuse 140°
13 20°   **29** 90°   **45** obtuse 120°
14 90°   **30** 140°   **46** obtuse 170°
15 40°   **31** 60°   **47** acute 50°
16 150°   **32** 100°   **48** obtuse 150°

B

1 acute   **9** 45°   **17** 105°   **25** 35°
2 obtuse   **10** 160°   **18** 145°   **26** 165°
3 acute   **11** 85°   **19** 70°   **27** 5°
4 obtuse   **12** 175°   **20** 120°   **28** 125°
5 obtuse   **13** 15°   **21** 20°   **29** 85°
6 acute   **14** 95°   **22** 75°   **30** 135°
7 acute   **15** 55°   **23** 110°   **31** 60°
8 obtuse   **16** 25°   **24** 155°   **32** 95°
39 180°   **43** acute 55°   **47** obtuse 105°
40 360°   **44** obtuse 135°   **48** acute 85°
41 acute 35°   **45** acute 65°   **49** obtuse 165°
42 obtuse 115°   **46** obtuse 95°   **50** obtuse 145°

c

1 51°   **7** 168°   **13** 12°   **19** 150°
2 31°   **8** 138°   **14** 126°   **20** 88°
3 30°   **9** 93°   **15** 129°   **21** 42°
4 66°   **10** 54°   **16** 73°   **22** 149°
5 114°   **11** 7°   **17** 87°   **23** 173°
6 107°   **12** 92°   **18** 138°   **24** 42°
(**25 to 32** allow +/− 10°)
25 140°   **27** 300°   **29** 320°   **31** 340°
26 270°   **28** 240°   **30** 80°   **32** 210°

page 113

A

1 a 30°   **3** c 100°   **5** e 115°   **7** g 125°
2 b 70°   **4** d 120°   **6** f 55°   **8** h 85°

B

1 i 105°   **3** k 132°   **5** m 121°   **7** o 143°
2 j 44°   **4** l 38°   **6** n 26°   **8** p 67°

C

1 q 40°   **3** s 46°   **5** u 287°   **7** w 112°
2 r 53°   **4** t 47°   **6** v 213°   **8** x 104°

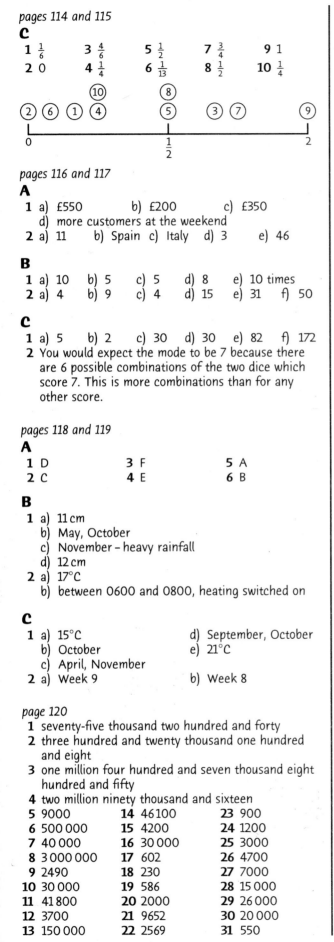

pages 114 and 115

C

1 $\frac{1}{6}$ 3 $\frac{4}{6}$ 5 $\frac{1}{2}$ 7 $\frac{3}{4}$ 9 1

2 0   4 $\frac{1}{4}$ 6 $\frac{1}{13}$ 8 $\frac{1}{2}$ 10 $\frac{1}{4}$

pages 116 and 117

A

1 a) £550   b) £200   c) £350

  d) more customers at the weekend

2 a) 11   b) Spain c) Italy   d) 3   e) 46

B

1 a) 10   b) 5   c) 5   d) 8   e) 10 times

2 a) 4   b) 9   c) 4   d) 15   e) 31   f) 50

C

1 a) 5   b) 2   c) 30   d) 30   e) 82   f) 172

2 You would expect the mode to be 7 because there
  are 6 possible combinations of the two dice which
  score 7. This is more combinations than for any
  other score.

pages 118 and 119

A

1 D   3 F   5 A

2 C   4 E   6 B

B

1 a) 11 cm
  b) May, October
  c) November – heavy rainfall
  d) 12 cm

2 a) 17°C
  b) between 0600 and 0800, heating switched on

C

1 a) 15°C   d) September, October
  b) October   e) 21°C
  c) April, November

2 a) Week 9   b) Week 8

page 120

1 seventy-five thousand two hundred and forty

2 three hundred and twenty thousand one hundred
  and eight

3 one million four hundred and seven thousand eight
  hundred and fifty

4 two million ninety thousand and sixteen

5 9000   14 46 100   23 900
6 500 000   15 4200   24 1200
7 40 000   16 30 000   25 3000
8 3 000 000 17 602   26 4700
9 2490   18 230   27 7000
10 30 000   19 586   28 15 000
11 41 800   20 2000   29 26 000
12 3700   21 9652   30 20 000
13 150 000   22 2569   31 550

32 780   33 50   34 70   35 200   36 350

37 A −16   B −2   C 6   D 14

38 14   39 8   40 22   41 16

42 −6, −3, −2, 0, 1, 5

43 21, 36, 45, 60

44 28, 36, 56, 60

45 21, 28, 56

46 45, 60

47 18, 36, etc.

48 24, 48, etc.

49 28, 56, etc.

50 30, 60, etc.

51 1, 2, 11, 22

52 1, 2, 4, 7, 14, 28

53 1, 2, 3, 5, 6, 10, 15, 30

54 1, 2, 3, 4, 6, 9, 12, 18, 36

55 1, 3, 9, 27

56 1, 2, 3, 6, 7, 14, 21, 42

57 1, 2, 4, 5, 8, 10, 20, 40

58 1, 3, 5, 7, 15, 21, 35, 105

59 16

60 49

61 100

62 64

63 61, 68, 75, 82

64 0·9, 1·1, 1·3, 1·5

65 −14, −17, −20, −23

66 63, 54, 45, 36

67 75, 90, 105, 120

68 −2, 0, 2, 4

69 48, 40, 32, 24

70 450, 500, 550, 600

page 121

A

1 $\frac{2}{4}$ 10 $\frac{3}{10}, \frac{2}{5}, \frac{1}{2}$ 19 $\frac{8}{3}$ 28 6

2 $\frac{2}{8}$ 11 $3\frac{1}{2}$ 20 $\frac{19}{4}$ 29 $\frac{7}{100}$

3 $\frac{3}{6}$ 12 $2\frac{1}{4}$ 21 $\frac{71}{10}$ 30 $\frac{5}{10}$

4 $\frac{5}{10}$ 13 $3\frac{2}{3}$ 22 $\frac{23}{6}$ 31 5

5 $\frac{4}{10}$ 14 $1\frac{3}{5}$ 23 $\frac{43}{8}$ 32 $\frac{1}{10}$

6 $\frac{4}{6}$ 15 $2\frac{5}{8}$ 24 $\frac{137}{100}$ 33 $\frac{6}{100}$

7 $\frac{6}{8}$ 16 $4\frac{1}{6}$ 25 $\frac{32}{5}$ 34 $\frac{7}{10}$

8 $\frac{8}{10}$ 17 $3\frac{7}{10}$ 26 $\frac{43}{9}$

9 $\frac{1}{2}, \frac{5}{8}, \frac{3}{4}$ 18 $2\frac{49}{100}$ 27 $\frac{9}{10}$

35 A 0·2   D 0·93
   B 0·5   E 0·99
   C 0·75   F 1·07

36 2·47, 2·7, 4·27, 4·72   43 5 m

37 1·59, 1·9, 5·19, 5·91   44 10 m

38 3·68, 3·8, 6·38, 6·8   45 £12

39 5·3, 5·37, 5·7, 5·73   46 £6

40 3 m   47 £30

41 3 m   48 £87

42 7 m   49 £5

50 a) $\frac{1}{2}$ 52 a) $\frac{7}{10}$ 54 a) $\frac{2}{5}$
   b) 0·5   b) 0·7   b) 0·4
   c) 50%   c) 70%   c) 40%

51 a) $\frac{3}{4}$ 53 a) $\frac{37}{100}$ 55 a) $\frac{83}{100}$
   b) 0·75   b) 0·37   b) 0·83
   c) 75%   c) 37%   c) 83%

56 50   60 5 cm   64 7   68 45p

57 150   61 90 cm   65 9   69 £1·20

58 24   62 21p   66 16   70 £2·75

59 12   63 48p   67 £1·50

page 122

A

1 730   9 600 − 86   17 644

2 93   10 8·4 − 7·6   18 173

3 6·3 + 0·7   11 810 − 340   19 456

4 38 + 62   12 272 − 57   20 233

5 747 + 500   13 713   21 1800

6 77 + 49   14 891   22 4011

7 7·3   15 1135   23 £4·88

8 56   16 1372   24 £6·86

25 1565
26 1483
27 £2·44
28 20·6
29 294
30 192
31 0·7 × 4
32 12 × 0
33 9 × 6
34 0·6 × 3
35 60
36 9
37 48 ÷ 8
38 150 ÷ 5

39 20 ÷ 5
40 31 ÷ 10
41 768
42 2286
43 4296
44 2583
45 16 r 2
46 28 r 4
47 14 r 5
48 34 r 6
49 816
50 2700
51 16·2
52 25·2

53 43·5
54 41·4
55 $5\frac{5}{7}$
56 $26\frac{3}{10}$
57 $7\frac{4}{9}$
58 $6\frac{3}{8}$
59 42·5
60 31·9
61 £1·80
62 £2·60
63 3600
64 21
65 115
66 215

page 123
1 4300 m
2 5·87 km
3 1·94 m
4 260 cm
5 5 mm
6 7·9 cm
7 382 m
8 7·8 km
9 6250 g
10 2300 g
11 3·74 kg
12 0·5 kg
13 1400 ml
14 3860 ml
15 2·9 l
16 0·48 l
17 A 2·3 m
   B 2·7 m
18 C 35 mm
   D 55 mm
19 E 150 g
   F 300 g
20 G 0·7 l
   H 1·6 l
21 800 ml
22 1·72 m
23 4·5 kg
24 20
25 6 cm²
26 10 cm
27 a) 24 cm², 20 cm   b) 49 cm², 28 cm
28 10 000 m²
29 3 years
30 104 weeks
31 6 weeks
32 72 hours
33 390 mins.
34 5 mins.
35 400 years
36 150 mins.
37 Tuesday
38 Saturday
39 Sunday
40 Thursday

41

12-HOUR CLOCK	24-HOUR CLOCK
4:25 p.m.	16:25
10:30 a.m.	10:30
7:15 p.m.	19:15
8:42 a.m.	08:42
9:06 p.m.	21:06
2:55 a.m.	02:55
11:37 a.m.	11:37
5:21 p.m.	17:21
7:49 a.m.	07:49
11:11 p.m.	23:11

page 124
1 irregular quadrilateral
2 regular pentagon
3 scalene triangle
4 irregular hexagon
5 isosceles triangle
6 irregular quadrilateral
7 regular octagon
8 irregular pentagon
9 a) 4, 6, 8   b) 1, 4, 7   c) 2, 7
14 tetrahedron
15 cylinder
16 pentagonal prism
17 cuboid
18 octahedron
19 triangular prism
20 cone
21 square-based pyramid
22 14
23 13
25 acute
26 obtuse
27 obtuse
28 acute
29 105°
30 31°
31 127°
32 69°
33 54°
34 96°
35 23°
36 138°

page 125
1 a) 9°C   b) Wednesday   c) 16°C
3 a) 5   b) 16   c) 6   d) 1   e) 60   f) 5
4 a) 40   b) 6   c) 5   d) 3   e) 70   f) 220

page 126
TEST 1
1 2017
2 123
3 4000
4 0·7
5 1·72 m
6 270°
7 37
8 0·75
9 50
10 19:25
11 38%
12 400 cm²
13 470
14 25
15 19
16 −3°C
17 $2\frac{1}{4}$
18 36 000
19 800 ml
20 4
21 49
22 1520
23 9
24 150

TEST 2
1 2·4
2 30%
3 280
4 47
5 12 009
6 63
7 400 g
8 254
9 1h 55 mins
10 9·5
11 13
12 4
13 30°
14 760
15 138
16 6°C
17 40 cm
18 2
19 Wednesday
20 25p
21 0·42
22 $\frac{12}{7}$
23 64
24 380 m

page 127
A
1 4 and 9
2 8 and 11
3 7 and 8
4 6 and 6
5 3 and 9
6 9 and 20
7 3 and 14
8 5 and 20
9 6 and 9
10 3 and 15

B
1 29
2 64
3 43
4 550
5 56
6 17
7 99
8 81

C
1 a) 11, 12   f) 32, 33
   b) 13, 14   g) 18, 19
   c) 29, 30   h) 36, 37
   d) 21, 22   i) 39, 40
   e) 16, 17
2 a) 5, 13   f) 11, 43
   b) 3, 23   g) 3, 37
   c) 5, 17   h) 7, 31
   d) 7, 17   i) 29, 61
   e) 13, 41
3 a) 35 + 16 − 7   f) 15 × 6 ÷ 10
   b) 72 − 19 + 12   g) 60 ÷ 3 × 5
   c) 10 + 47 − 21   h) 48 ÷ 6 × 9
   d) 12 × 6 ÷ 8   i) 5 ÷ 10 × 6
   e) 7 × 4 ÷ 2

page 128
A
1 46 + 63
2 37 + 93
3 58 + 27
4 73 + 12
5 59 + 36
6 86 + 52
7 69 + 74
8 96 + 38
9 46 − 38
10 43 − 25
11 194 − 75
12 50 − 43
13 92 − 56
14 167 − 82
15 118 − 47

Answers

B

1
```
   2 3 6
 + 1 7 2
   4 0 8
```

5
```
   3 1 6
 - 2 5 3
     6 3
```

9
```
      5 7
 ×      6
   3 4 2
```

2
```
   4 7 4
 - 1 2 9
   3 4 5
```

6
```
      8 6
 ×      4
   3 4 4
```

10
```
   3 4 9
 + 3 5 6
   7 0 5
```

3
```
      6 7
 ×      2
   1 3 4
```

7
```
   5 8 3
 + 1 7 8
   7 6 1
```

11
```
   5 8 5
 - 1 2 6
   4 5 9
```

4
```
   3 5 8
 + 2 0 5
   5 6 3
```

8
```
   6 9 1
 - 2 7 8
   4 1 3
```

12
```
      3 9
 ×      3
   1 1 7
```

C

1
```
   3 2 6
 - 1 7 4
   1 5 2
```

5
```
   2 3 9
 ×      6
 1 4 3 4
```

9
```
      9 4
 6)5 6 4
```

2
```
      4 2 7
 ×        3
   1 2 8 1
```

6
```
      5 7
 4)2 2 8
```

10
```
   4 1 4
 - 1 4 8
   2 6 6
```

3
```
      5 3
 3)1 5 9
```

7
```
   5 3 1
 - 4 5 7
     7 4
```

11
```
   1 8 4
 ×      7
 1 2 8 8
```

4
```
   2 4 5
 - 1 6 9
     7 6
```

8
```
      5 3 3
 ×        4
   2 1 3 2
```

12
```
      2 8
 5)1 4 0
```